# The River World and Other Explorations

A JOAN KAHN BOOK

## BOOKS BY BERTON ROUECHÉ

### *Fiction*

BLACK WEATHER

THE LAST ENEMY

FERAL

FAGO

### *Nonfiction*

THE RIVER WORLD AND OTHER EXPLORATIONS

ELEVEN BLUE MEN

THE INCURABLE WOUND

THE DELECTABLE MOUNTAINS

A MAN NAMED HOFFMAN

THE NEUTRAL SPIRIT

WHAT'S LEFT

THE ORANGE MAN

# The River World and Other Explorations

## Berton Roueché

HARPER & ROW, PUBLISHERS
New York, Hagerstown, San Francisco, London

The contents of this book first appeared in *The New Yorker.*

FIRST EDITION

*Designer: Eve Callahan*
*Production editor: William Monroe*

Library of Congress Cataloging in Publication Data

Roueché, Berton, 1911–
    The river world and other explorations.
    Articles originally published in the New Yorker.
    Contents: The Places: The river world. First boat to King Island. The steeple.
A window on the Oligocene. A natural miracle.—The edibles: One hundred thousand
varieties. A friend in disguise. The humblest fruit.—The people: Schönheit muss leiden.
The grower's shadow. Forty flights of steps. The good news. Solo.
    I. Title.
PS3535.0845R5        818'.5'407        78–4738
ISBN 0–06–013686–3

78 79 80 81 82 10 9 8 7 6 5 4 3 2 1

# Contents

## I. The Places

## II. The Edibles

## III. The People

# I. The Places

# The River World

The Lesta K., a square-nosed, diesel-powered towboat owned and operated by the Port City Barge Line, of Greenville, Mississippi, is pushing slowly down the Missouri River toward St. Louis behind a tow of big red hopper barges loaded with Nebraska wheat and Kansas flour. There are eight barges in the tow—each riding nine feet deep in the water under fifteen hundred tons of cargo—and they are lashed two abreast. They form a raft-like mass just about seventy feet wide and almost eight hundred feet long. At the head of the tow, where I am sitting on a coil of rigging near the bow of the starboard barge, there is the feel of a raft—a peaceful sense of drifting, a sense of country quiet. The only sound is the slap of water under the rake of the bow. I am alone and half asleep in the silence and the warmth of the mild midmorning sun. The river is empty. There is only the bend ahead and the bend behind, a sandy shore of brush and willows on the near bank, and a steep bluff crowned with cottonwoods a quarter of a mile away on the other—no towns, no houses, no bridges, no roads, not even another boat. Early this morning, after a night tied up in fog at Kansas City, we passed the mouth of the Big Blue River (originally La Rivière de l'Eau Bleue), where, one June day in 1804, the expedition headed by Meriwether Lewis and William Clark "saw a number of parroquets *(Conurus carolinensis),* and killed some deer." There are no longer any parakeets along the Missouri River (or anywhere else in America), but its shores still look as wild as they were at the turn of the eighteenth century.

I was going to St. Louis, to Cairo, to Memphis, to Natchez, to Baton Rouge, to New Orleans—I was going down the river as far as I could go. I was going as far as I could find a towboat to carry me. The packet boat has vanished from America. It has gone the way the passenger train is going. It was too slow, too comfortable, too restful. But freight still moves on the rivers. The volume, in fact, increases every year. And one can sometimes arrange for accommodations on a towboat.

I had arranged to meet the Lesta K. at a grain-and-molasses dock some twenty river miles above Kansas City. That was late yesterday afternoon. A friend drove me out from the city, and I was waiting on the dock when the Lesta K. and its thrusting tow came into view, sliding downstream on a long crossing where the channel switched from one bank to the other. The Lesta K. was built in 1942, but its lines are still the standard lines for towboats on the rivers. I watched it lift into sight. First, a high white pilothouse with a narrow open bridge all around and a complex of whistles and fog bells and searchlights and radio and radar antennas on the roof above. Then an open texas deck. Then the boiler deck, with a small cluster of cabins forward and two faintly fuming smokestacks aft. Then the main deck, running the length of the boat (about a hundred and fifty feet), with a deckhouse almost as long. The main deck was just above water level—there was hardly three feet of free-board—with two tall, bumper-like towing knees at the bow. The whistle blew. I waved. A deckhand with long, sandy hair and a horse-shoe mustache waved back. He wore a T-shirt with a peace symbol on the front. The Lesta K. nudged gently against the dock.

The deckhand gave me a hand aboard, and took me up to a cabin on the boiler deck. Behind the ferocious mask of hair and mustache was a smiling, boyish face. And he wasn't a deckhand; he was the second mate, and his name was Johnny Avent. My cabin was at the bow, just under the pilothouse, and the roar of the engines was only a distant hum. There was a single bed, a chest of drawers, a chair and a desk, a *Playboy* calendar on the wall. An inner door opened on a bathroom with a sign above the washbasin: "Potable

Water." I left my bag and followed Avent down and aft to the galley. It was six o'clock, and supper was just over. Supper is at five-thirty on the river. (So is breakfast, and dinner is at eleven-thirty.) We passed the last of the five-man forward watch—the six-to-noon and six-to-midnight watch—coming along the passage. None of them looked much older than the second mate. The remains of supper were still on the table: a platter with one surviving breaded veal cutlet; dishes of peas and carrots, lima beans, green beans, creamed corn, boiled cabbage, mashed potatoes, potato chips, chili con carne, cottage cheese, and combination salad; three big biscuits on a tray; half a poundcake; a bowl of whipped cream, a bowl of canned peaches; a pitcher of iced tea, a pitcher of Kool-Aid. The cook brought me a plate and a glass of ice. He was a big man with a big pale, worried face, and his name was Malone—H. L. Malone. "Or maybe you'd rather have coffee?" he said. I said I preferred iced tea. He nodded. "Yeah," he said. "Real fine." He sat down at the head of the table and gazed at a notice framed on the wall: "Pilot Rules for the Western Rivers & the Red River of the North." He frowned.

"They drink a lot of coffee on the river," he said. "Yeah—and the farther south, the more they drink. Now, I'm from Mississippi myself, but I give it up. I stopped last March, and I'll tell you something: no more heartburn. It cured it just like that. The same doctor told me to try corn oil for frying. He said it was a whole lot better. So I don't fry nothing no more in hog lard. Yeah—and another thing I learned. This was when I had me a little drive-in down home in Lexington. I used to sell a lot of pickled hard-boiled eggs. I sold dozens of them every week. But you know how hard a boiled egg is to shell. I spent half my time just peeling them eggs. Then the farmer I was buying from he give me a tip. Pip them, he said. Punch a little dent in one end before you cook them. And, sure enough, they peel just like a banana. But I don't grudge the fellas their coffee. I know they like it when they go on watch, and they like it when they come off watch, and they also like it in between. So I've always got a big pot on the stove. They don't allow no liquor on the river. That's the company rule. And no gambling, either. Coffee gives the fellas something to do. The only other thing is eating. The way it works, a fella works for thirty days straight and then he's off for fifteen days, and I try to keep them happy when they're on the boat. You know what they say: a full stomach makes a patient man. There's ten of us on this boat. There's the captain and his relief. There's the chief engineer and his relief. The rest are crew and me. I will say the company understands about food. They know it's important, and they allow me around a thousand dollars a month to work with. You wait till tomorrow. Saturday dinner is the high point of the week on the river. Steak—T-bone steak, with mushrooms. All you want. I broil a couple of dozen. I fry my chicken and my pork chops and my catfish, but I broil my steak. I've been on the river for nine years—seven with Port City—and I've got my own way of doing things. I like it on the river. Of course, I don't have my wife anymore. She left me—after seventeen years of marriage. I don't think it was the river. These days, I could sleep in the morning till maybe four-fifteen, but I like to get up around three. I don't like to go right to work. I like to set around and drink tea and wake up good. I take my tea and go out on deck and set there. I like the dark and the smell of the river. And I don't let nothing bother me."

I climbed two flights of almost vertical stairs to the aerie of the pilothouse. The stairs were dark, and the pilothouse was dim with dusk and cigarette smoke. Jene Bills, the captain, was sitting there alone in the twilight at a console of levers and grips and gears and meters—a square-built man of about forty-five with smooth brown hair and a broken nose. His chair was a big leather armchair as high as a shoeshine chair, and it gave him a commanding view through the windows all around. I cleared away a pile of charts and magazines and sat down on a high wooden bench. The river spreading out ahead had a coppery sunset glitter. Bills craned his neck and grunted. "A lot of pilots cuss this time of day," he said. "I mean this doggone glare. But fog is worse. We've got radar—the screen is that box standing over there. We couldn't run at night without it. But radar ain't enough in fog—not on this river. The Missouri is too fast and too narrow, and the bends are too short. It's got a lot of bends that ain't but two miles long. You've got to do a lot of holding back—what we call backing up. I know a lot of pilots on the Lower River—on the Mississippi on down from Cairo—that are scared shirtless on this river. I've got a good feeling for it, but I will admit it can be trouble. It can be real hard work to go down. When you're moving along at eight or nine or even ten miles an hour and there isn't too much water in the channel, anything can happen. Like finding a bar built up on a crossing that wasn't there before. The most important tool we've got is the swing indicator. It's like a gyrocompass. It tells me if the tow is swinging out of line. It's a whole lot faster than my eye. I watch that machine as much as I watch the river. But the river is getting better, too. The Army Engineers have done a lot to stabilize the banks and maintain a decent channel. This channel used to change a couple of times a day. And the Coast Guard keeps the channel marked with buoys—like that red nun off to port. But this is still the trickiest river in the U.S.A. Coming up, it don't matter. You're poking along at three or four miles an hour. There's nothing much for the pilot to do but set back and read his Western magazine. No close work, and plenty of time to act if need be. I mean, when you cut your engines, the current is as good as a brake. But, going down, you can stub your toe pretty easy. When your tow is put together right, when you've secured your barges end to end and side to side and the stern of the tow is fast to the tow knees—when you've done all that, why, it's just like one big boat, and it steers like one. It don't act or feel much different. But you've got to remember one thing. It's one hell of a big old boat. You can't stop it or turn it like you would your car. Not unless you want to bust it up."

The sunset glare was fading from the river. The shadows deepened along the banks. Then the last of the light was suddenly gone, and the river was only a stir of paler dark. Three little running lights appeared on the faraway head of the tow. Bills turned on a searchlight. The beam reached out across the tow through a turmoil of white willow flies. It touched a bobbing black can buoy, then a ghostly finger of sandy shoal, then a bright-green jungle wall of trees. It felt back across the water and pounced on another buoy. "Another thing about this river," Bills said. "I think it's probably the cleanest. Up at Sioux City and all the way down to Omaha, it's as clear and blue as a lake. It's the prettiest, too. I guess I've been on most. The Upper Mississippi and the Lower. The Ohio. The Illinois. The Tennessee. If you want to know the truth, I've been on the river all of my life. I was born on a houseboat down at Memphis. And I guess you could say that the river was my salvation. I never had a father. I only had a stepfather, and when my mother left us, he raised me. He worked as a steeplejack when he worked. I done the rest—the cooking, the washing, the housekeeping, the woodchopping. That man never let up. He treated me worse than the meanest man would treat the sorriest dog. When I reached sixteen, I dropped out of school and run off down the river. I started out where everybody starts on the river—as a deckhand. That's the school for the river. There ain't no other. You learn to be a pilot by learning the river and watching the pilot work. Johnny Avent, the boy that brought you aboard, I'm teaching him right now. When you've made ten round trips on your river and can draw a map of its course and put in every bend by name and every light and every crossing, then you can take the Coast Guard examination. If you pass, you're a licensed pilot on that river. That's what I done. Those were still the steamboat days. I remember that long, lonesome whistle on those old steamers. It was a beautiful sound coming across the water. It was sad, but it made you feel good. There wasn't much else in those days that you'd want to brag about. Everything was different then. The river was just about the bottom of the gutter. Hell, it *was* the bottom. If you worked on the river, you were trash. People would walk away from you. But it gets you, the river. I had it in me too deep to let me quit, and I got my first license in 1950. Then things began to change. Business got better, and the pay and everything else got better, and they started crying for pilots. There still aren't near enough for the need. Last year, more than fifteen per cent of all the freight that moved in this country was carried by barge, and it's going to be more this year. The reason is the rates are so low—three mills per ton-mile. The railroads, for example, charge the shipper fifteen. There's a lot of new people coming on the river now. We're even getting college men—fellas like Johnny. They're ambitious to learn and advance. Of course, we get the other kind, too. I mean that new kind of kid they've got these days. They don't know nothing, and they don't want to learn. They don't want to work. All they want is easy living. Eat, sleep, and make a payday. Then they're long gone. And do you know the pay a deckhand gets now? Twenty-two fifty a day. That's almost seven hundred dollars for the thirty days. And no expenses—no room, no board, no nothing. They make me sick. We call this here a bulkhead and we call what we're standing on a deck. They can't be bothered. They call it walls and floor.

They call the bow the front end and the head the bathroom and the galley the kitchen. And they're not all kids. Some of them are grown men. I had a mate a while back who kept talking about the capsule. I asked him what the hell was that. He said, 'Why, that thing there.' And he pointed to the capstan."

Bills reached across the console and picked up a microphone. He pressed a switch. "Johnny?" he said, and his voice splintered out from a speaker on the bridge. "Polka Dots? One of you fellas. The captain wants some coffee." He glanced at me, but I shook my head and he put the microphone back. "Coffee gets to be a habit on the river," he said. "I seem to need it even when I'm relaxed at home. I sometimes wake up in the night and go out to the kitchen and make myself a cup. It drives my wife about crazy. But now I'm going to show you something pretty. We're coming into Kansas City. It's just around this bend, and, lighted up at night, it's the prettiest skyline on the river. I've seen them all, and nothing else can touch it." We picked our way through a crossing and into a tight hairpin bend. There was a glow above the riverside woods ahead. We came out of the bend, and there it was—an explosion of lights, mirrored in the dark of the river and diffused across the sky, climbing steeply up a terraced bluff to a soaring summit of flashing signs and floodlit towers. I looked up at Kansas City and thought of "Huckleberry Finn": "The fifth night we passed St. Louis, and it was like the whole world lit up." So was Kansas City.

A voice from the pilothouse speaker called me back to the boat from my seat at the head of the tow. It was eleven-thirty and time for dinner. I walked back along the barges through a spillage history of past and present cargoes—wheat, rock salt, soybeans, phosphate rock, corn. I ate my T-bone steak (and five vegetables, baked potato, green salad, hot biscuits, vanilla ice cream) with the forward watch. They were Bills, Johnny Avent, the chief engineer, and two young deckhands—the one called Polka Dots, because he wore a red-and-white polka-dot cap, and another called Tear Drops, because soon after he came aboard the Lesta K. he received a shattering "Dear John" letter. Just beyond the windows at the end of the table, a long green shore of willows drifted serenely by. It was practically in the room. We sat at the table until well past noon. There was a somnolent feeling of Sunday. Afternoon is often an idle time on the river. The forward watch goes off to bed for its second installment of sleep. "What I like to do," Bills said as he pushed back his chair, "is get into bed with a good Luke Short or Frank O'Rourke or one of those, and the next thing I know, they're knocking on the door to get me up for supper." With nothing much to do, the after watch lie around on deck and smoke and talk and turn the pages of *Playboy* and *Cavalier* and *Penthouse.* Only the pilot—the relief captain—is fully awake and at work. Even the cook goes off to his room for a nap.

The pilot on the Lesta K. was a man named David Evans. He was a handsome, red-faced man of about thirty-five with long gray hair and with a heart tattooed on his thumb. When I came into the pilothouse, he was staring out at the river and whistling some tuneless tune. He had a mug of coffee on the console beside him, and a textbook—"The Hive and the Honey Bee." "Beekeeping is one of my hobbies," he said. "It's an interest. I got three hundred hives down home in Mississippi—down in Choctaw County. I get a good hundred pounds of sweet-clover honey per hive. But there's so much poison in the fields these days you can't let your bees stray. You got to keep them close to home. The way you do that is plant good nectar sources nearby. The next thing I think I'll do is get me a herd of Black Angus cattle. And I want to build me a nice big home—a fifty-thousand-dollar home. But my real life is here on the river. I been on the river ten years, and I like it real fine. It's a world of its own. It's a world I feel comfortable in. The Missouri is the friendliest river. Everybody knows everybody else. Nobody wants to cut your throat. I got a first cousin who's a captain on the Lower River. His mother was a real Christian woman. I mean, she had the power of prayer. When we were all growing up, my cousin he cut his middle finger off. The blood was gushing out, but his mother she started praying and the bleeding stopped. I mean it stopped. I remember seeing it with my own eyes. But most of those pilots on the Lower River, they don't like it much up here. This river is too fast for them. You know what they call the Missouri—they call it the Big Muddy. They used to say it was too thick to run and too thin to plow. But that ain't true no more. They've cleaned it up. But it's fast. I've averaged twelve to fourteen miles an hour going down with eight barges. That was high water—in May or June. Of course, I've also busted up some tows. It's three hundred and sixty-seven river miles from Kansas City to the mouth, just above St. Louis, and one trip I busted up seventeen times. It made a real long trip, chasing and catching and tying up those runaway barges. It took me seven days instead of two or three."

Evans sat up higher in his chair. He reached for a pair of binoculars and trained them down the river. There was a dark spot on the moving water far ahead. "Somebody coming," he said. "But we got the right-of-way. The down boat always has the right-of-way." He picked up a telephone and turned a radio dial. "Lesta K. to westbound tow coming into Wakenda Chute. Over."

A voice came out of a speaker: "Belzoni to Lesta K. How you doing, Dave?"

"Real fine, old buddy. How's it look down there?"

"Had a little trouble in Bushwhacker. It's shallow, Dave. Real shallow."

"O.K., old buddy. I gotcha."

"Yeah. But, you know—no problem. How you want to pass?"

"I'll give you the bank. Port to port. One whistle."

"Gotcha, Dave. Say hello to everybody."

"Real fine, Skip. Will do. And the same to you."

I watched the Belzoni coming. It loomed slowly into shape. It came creeping up along the shore on the left behind a tow of eight barges. One of them carried a massive angularity of structural steel—a section of a bridge. Evans pulled a single blast on the whistle. The Belzoni replied. We came closely abreast, the Lesta K. moving at what looked like breakneck speed. Evans jumped out of his chair and stepped out on the bridge and waved. A man in a white shirt with the tails hanging loose waved back from the bridge of the Belzoni.

The river stretched bright and empty again. The green shores—bluff and bottom, bottom and bluff—ran on and on and on. I watched a flight of seven sandhill cranes flapping from shoal to shoal. There was a volume of charts on the bench where I sat: "Missouri River Navigation Charts: Kansas City, Missouri, to the Mouth." Every bend, every crossing, every light was marked. I turned the pages, following the names downriver. Like all place names, they were a kind of poetry. Teteseau, Chamois, Cote Sans Dessein, Creve Coeur, St. Aubert,

Auxvasse, Gasconade, Bonhomme. Tamerlane, Amazon, Malta, Eu-
phrase, Miami. Berger, Bernheimer, Hermann, Berlin. Slaughter-
house, Plow Boy, Bushwhacker, Rising Creek, Cowmire, Centaur,
Pelican. The afternoon crawled peacefully away. Wilhoite, Lupus,
Mullanphy, Diana.

I saw just three towns between Kansas City and the river mouth,
below St. Charles. I had a passing view of the once premier port of
Boonville (where in October of 1864 Price's Confederate Missourians,
marching victoriously up the river to Gettysburgian defeat in the
three-day Battle of Westport, paused for a spell of roistering rest,
one of them leaving behind an unfinished letter: "Wee hav plenty
of corn bred and pore beefe to eat and sasafras tee to drink"); Jefferson
City, the capital (with the lanterned dome of the State Capitol,
the mansard roof of the Governor's Mansion, and the battlements
of the State Penitentiary strung along a landscaped bluff); and the
tidy red brick waterfront of the old German town of Hermann. We
stopped at none of them, but a mile or two above Hermann the
Irene E., from Staude's Boat Supply Dock, came out to meet us.
That was late Sunday afternoon. I stood with Malone at the galley
door and watched the Irene E. approach. "Pete Staude is my grocery
store," Malone said. "I give him an order on one trip and pick it
up on the next. He's bringing me out just a few things now, but I
got a big order for him. All the boats trade with Pete. He handles
everything but liquor. He even does our laundry. And he's where
we get our mail." The Lesta K. slowed to the speed of the current,
and the Irene E. came alongside. Two after-watch deckhands made
it secure. We floated on together. A man in a business suit handed
up a heavy crate and a bundle of mail tied with string.

"I hope for once you brought me the right kind of peas," Malone
said. "I mean them little ones, Pete."

"You got them, old buddy," Staude said. "And everything else
you ordered."

"It better not be them big-as-chinaberry kind."

"I even got the Sunday paper for you," Staude said. "Now, who
needs what?"

Somebody broke the string on the parcel and spread out the mail
on the dining table. The crew, both watches—everybody but Evans,
up in the pilothouse—crowded around. There were typewritten bills

and business letters addressed in pencil and big, thick letters in scented envelopes addressed in colored ink. The deckhand called Tear Drops had one of the scented letters, and he turned his back and stood in a corner to read it. Johnny Avent had three.

Before going down to bed that night, I went out on the bridge for a breath of river air, and heard a kind of music. It was a whining and whanging and thumping, and it came from the main deck, below. I leaned over the rail and looked down on Johnny Avent and two deckhands. Johnny was sitting on a box with the blade of a carpenter's saw bent against the deck like a musical saw, and he was tapping it with a hammer. The deckhands were dancing—stomping and whirling and clapping their hands. It gave me a curious feeling, a curious start of memory. I remembered a painting by the mid-nineteenth-century genre painter George Caleb Bingham called "The Jolly Flat-boatmen," which shows the long-haired crew of a river scow cavorting on deck to the music of a fiddler. I looked down at the whining saw and the capering deckhands, and wondered again at how little the river seemed to change.

After breakfast (pineapple juice, oatmeal, ham and eggs and grits), I walked out to the head of the tow to watch the sun come up. The sky overhead was black and clear and full of stars, but a layer of fog hung, boiling like steam, on the river. I sat and watched the stars fade and the sky go gray and the first spread of pink appear. It was still dark, it still had the feel of night, and then suddenly it was morning. The sun was up, and the fog was thinning and opening and drifting away, and the grass along the steep right bank was dappled with dewy cobwebs.

I heard somebody coming up the middle of the tow. It was Johnny Avent, hunched under a braided ball of two-inch rope the size of a bushel basket. Behind him came the deckhand Polka Dots with another. They hung one ball over the side of the starboard barge and the other off the port barge. Johnny came over and sat down on the deck beside me. "Them?" he said. "They're bumpers. We hang them out whenever we go through a lock. On the Upper River and up on the Illinois, they're hanging there all the time. The Upper Mississippi is nothing but locks. There's only one lock on this run— the Chain of Rocks lock, just above St. Louis." He gave his cutthroat mustache a pull. "I guess you've heard of William Faulkner," he said. "And Eudora Welty? And William Alexander Percy? And Shelby Foote? And Hodding Carter? Then you probably know they're all Mississippians—and so am I. I come from Greenville. My daddy is port engineer for Port City. I guess that's why I'm on the river. He used to be a chief engineer, and all I ever heard since I was a little bitty boy was the river. I didn't always act like it, though. I studied architectural engineering at college—at Southern Mississippi—and I had a rock band there. I play piano and organ, and like that. I gigged in high school and college both. We played those long weekends. We'd play some college down in Louisiana and then cut over to Texas and come back by way of Alabama or Tennessee. I got me an ulcer, and my grades went down, so I finally quit. The other fellas, they're still playing, but my real world was always the river. I worked here summers, and I've been on the river full time since I got out of school last year. Captain Easy—that's what we call Captain Bills; there's another captain we call Captain Rough— he's teaching me to be a pilot. I like this peaceful life. It's peaceful, but it isn't lonely. I like the way you've always got somebody to horse around with and throw the bull with. And I like the money, too. I get twenty-seven eighty-five a day—that's the rate for a second mate—and it's all clear money. I mean, I haven't got anybody, and when I'm home I live with my daddy and mummy. I don't even smoke. It's nice to have that big old roll of money. You go in a local bar and start flashing a few fifties around, and those chicks, they kind of go for that. It's like being in the band again, the way those chicks come running, only better. You don't have to pack right up and drive to, like, Shreveport. I like money. But, thank God, I didn't sell my body that time. The medical school down at Louisiana State was offering three hundred dollars apiece for bodies to be claimed after death, and five of us drove down to New Orleans. We wanted that easy money for partying. But then we found out they were going to tattoo something on your heel for identification. I didn't like the idea of some girl getting into bed and looking down and reading my heel and thinking I'd been stole from some morgue."

I dropped the sports section of yesterday's St. Louis *Post-Dispatch* back on the pilothouse bench. I got up and stood at the window.

"It looks like the river is getting a little wider," I said.

"Wider?" Bills said.

"I don't know," I said. "It just seems wider than it was."

"Yeah," he said. "Well, it *is* wider. It's just about twice as wide. But it's a different river. We come out of the Missouri at that big long bend back there. That was the mouth. This here is the Mississippi."

I left the Lesta K. on Monday afternoon at St. Louis. As we came out of the lock at Chain of Rocks, Bills received a radioed order to exchange his barges there for another tow and return with it upriver to Kansas City. The Port City Barge Line had made arrangements for me to continue my trip on another boat—the National Progress, of the National Marine Service, Inc., of St. Louis, H. P. Duplantis, captain. The National Progress was tied up just below the St. Louis waterfront, and the Lesta K. churned down there on its way to pick up its new tow—past the Eads Bridge (the first steel bridge built across the Mississippi, completed in 1874, built with arches high enough between the piers to clear the tall twin stacks of the paddle-wheel steamers), past the new soaring Saarinen wishbone arch, past the anchored replica of the Robert E. Lee, past the replica of the Santa Maria, past the five-deck excursion boat Admiral, past the floating restaurant Huck Finn, past the showboat Goldenrod. The National Progress stood offshore behind a tow of four shining doubletank refrigerated anhydrous-ammonia barges, flying the company's flag—a red beaver on a white background. We came alongside, and I stepped across the gap. A deckhand in bib overalls—a big, grumbling fat man—took me to my cabin and then on to the pilothouse. He climbed the steep stairs breathing hard and pulling at the seat of his pants. "I don't know about work clothes anymore," he said. "You can't get anything that will wear for more than forty-five minutes. I think the Mafia must have taken over the hole shebang."

The pilothouse was as loud and crowded as a cocktail party. There was Duplantis, a young Cajun with long black hair and bright blue eyes, sitting on the bench. There was the pilot, a young Mississippian named William McBunch, at the console. There was a refrigeration technician (anhydrous ammonia is ammonia liquefied by sub-zero cooling for safekeeping), a young Arkansan named Dennis Blackford.

There was a deckhand from Texas making coffee at a little stove in a corner, and a deckhand from Missouri. The fat deckhand and I brought the number in the little room to seven. Everybody was smoking and drinking coffee and talking at the top of his voice.

". . . and married a fella from Texas."

"It's a funny thing—you meet a fella from Texas, and if you call him Tex, he kind of preens. But you meet a fella from Arkansas and you call him Arkie—well, you got a fight on your hands."

"You ask me, I'd rather have a sister in a whorehouse than a brother in Texas."

"I don't know why they call a Cajun a 'coon-ass.' I never ate coon in my life."

"The way I heard it, every time you mention Missouri, a jackass will kneel down and pray."

I sat down on the bench, and one of the deckhands brought me a cup of coffee. It was black and strong, and sharp with chicory. The deckhand leaned on the arm of the bench.

"That's coon-ass coffee," he said. "That's what they call it. And we make it drip. But every captain on this line has his own idea about how to make his coffee. One captain has me make it one spoon of Luzianne and then one spoon of Community, then another spoon of Luzianne and another one of Community. And so on. And it has to be just right or he gets as mad as a mule."

"I remember one time," Duplantis said. "We took a new cook on at Memphis. One of the deckhands came running up here to the pilothouse and he said, 'Oh, Jesus, Duke, you won't believe it but that new cook she's a girl.' Well, I'd heard of women cooks on the river—a few old widows. But he was right. She came up to report, and she was a young girl. Good-looking, too, and built real nice. She said she had an aunt who had cooked on towboats. She said she had taken home economics in high school, and her aunt had taught her the rest. The aunt had told her about the different watches and when they ate and the kind of food, and about accommodating the crew. I said, 'The what?' The men, she said—about going to bed with the men. However, she said, her aunt had told her not to play any favorites. That could only cause trouble. She would take the fellas in turn when they wanted her. But she had one rule. Nobody but me was to know her last name or where she lived on shore.

And that's the way it was. She accommodated the fellas—practically the whole boat. But then the trouble began. It was just what she had tried to avoid. Dissension. They all of them fell in love with her, or thought they had, and in no time at all everybody—even the married men—was unhappy and jealous and snarling at everybody else. So when we got up to Marseilles, Illinois, I had to put her ashore. She was a real nice girl—real likable, and a good cook, too. But she was strange—real strange. I remember her name. It was Shirley."

"It was Shirley Ann," the Missouri deckhand said.

I had supper that night with the after watch (fried country ham and redeye gravy, sweet potatoes, succotash, okra, banana cream pie) and then sat for a while on the texas deck and watched a new moon rise. I saw what the early-Victorian novelist Captain Frederick Marryat had seen before me—had seen almost a century and a half before: "I did not expect that the muddy Mississippi would be able to reflect the silver light of the moon; yet it did, and the effect was very beautiful. Truly it may be said of this river, as it is of many ladies, that it is a candle-light beauty." I went down to bed before nine. The nights are short when you are called for breakfast at five o'clock. My cabin was over the engine room, and I awoke a dozen times to the grinding roar of the engines backing and braking, but only for a moment. The usual engine sound—the steady forward thrust—was a soporific hum.

Duplantis was alone in the pilothouse but was talking on the telephone when I climbed the stairs after breakfast. I stopped at the door that opened onto the bridge. The river was unmistakably the Mississippi now. It stretched a mile wide and infinitely on ahead. In the thin white early-morning light, it might have been a lake. But the banks were still riverbanks—sandbars and willow flats, willow slopes and high cottonwood bluffs.

"Yeah," Duplantis said on the telephone. "I gotcha, man. I'll just keep paddling." He hung up, and turned. "There's fresh coffee there on the stove. Or if you'd rather have a Coke, there's some in the refrigerator underneath. And you can pour me some more coffee while you're at it." He was wearing dark glasses, and his long dark hair hung down across one eye. "That's Pond Lily Light over there on the Missouri side. We made good time last night, in spite of a lot of fog—better than sixty miles a watch. We're past Cape Girardeau and we're getting close to Cairo. It's interesting there, the way the Ohio comes in. A lot of pilots think the books have got the rivers wrong. You can see it here on this chart. The Mississippi comes in from the west and the Ohio comes down from the north, and after they meet you can see how the Mississippi bends and runs due south. A lot of the pilots think the Ohio is the main river and the Mississippi is the feeder—the tributary. I think they've got a point. And here comes the fella I was talking to."

The tow came distantly into view, hugging the high Missouri shore—a tiny white pilothouse rising behind an acreage of barges. It came close enough for me to make out the head of the tow: it spread five barges wide. I took up a pair of binoculars and read the name on the pilothouse: Theresa Seley. Duplantis pulled the whistle twice, for a starboard-to-starboard passing. The Theresa Seley replied in confirmation, and came slowly up and slowly abreast and past. Duplantis raised a hand in the ritual greeting. I counted the barges. The tow was five barges wide and six barges long—a total of thirty barges. It *was* an acreage. It was five acres of barges. And, at fifteen hundred tons per barge, it carried thirty-five thousand tons of cargo. It was more cargo than could be moved by rail on a freight train of three hundred cars.

"Fellas new on the river are scared of certain cargoes," Duplantis said. "It scares them to handle oil or petrochemicals—chemicals of any kind. Those things are dangerous. Anhydrous ammonia is danger-ous. So you have to be careful. You have to follow the safety rules. But the kind of load that scares me most is something else entirely. If you noticed that boat, the Theresa Seley, he had a couple of deck barges loaded with river sand. That wet river sand is real unstable. It shifts. Even a gentle turn can shift the load, and a shift of fifteen hundred tons of sand—all that weight, with the buoyancy all under-neath—it can turn you right smack over. I've never had any trouble. I've never even come close, except once when I tried to keep from running down two measly little ducks. I've never had anything like a fire or explosion, but I had a tow one time where it would have been kind of interesting. That was up on the Upper River. I picked up a tow at St. Paul of eight barges of popping corn and a jumbo barge of soybean oil. All the way down to St. Louis, at every lock and every bend, I kept thinking, What if something happened? What if something exploded? What if we got hit by lightning? My God, the whole Middle West would be knee-deep in buttered popcorn!"

I left the National Progress around ten o'clock that morning off the village of Hickman, Kentucky, just north of the Tennessee line. The circumstances were much the same as those that had moved me to the Progress from the Lesta K.: an order had been telephoned to Duplantis to meet another National Marine Service towboat there—the National Gateway, Victor Wood, captain—transfer his tow to her, and return upriver to Hannibal. Arrangements had been made for me and the refrigeration technician, Blackford, to continue aboard the Gateway, destination Baton Rouge. The Gateway, built in 1966, was bigger and finer than the Progress, and my cabin was a guest stateroom—twin beds, a deep leather armchair, a reading lamp, a tiled bathroom hung with big, thick towels. Across the passageway was a lounge for the crew, with a sofa, comfortable chairs, a television set, and a table piled with paperback books (including "Ada," by Vladimir Nabokov, and Saul Bellow's "Herzog") and copies of the Memphis *Press-Scimitar* and Hodding Carter's Greenville *Delta Democrat-Times*. The boat gave a shudder. I looked out the window. We were under way—behind a seven-barge tow of anhydrous ammonia and caustic soda, with red metal danger flags standing stiff on every barge. I found the stairs to the pilothouse and went up. Wood—thirty-eight, green-eyed, tousle-haired, unshaven, sockless—was at the console. A gray-haired deckhand with a sunken jaw was sitting on the bench.

". . . seniority," the deckhand said. "That's what they say. Thirty minutes of kissing ass will do you more good than thirty years of seniority."

"Yeah?" Wood said. "Well, I tell you what. How about you going over there to the stove and pouring everybody a nice little cup of coffee?"

We moved around an overgrown towhead island and into a long starboard crossing. The Missouri shore loomed and lifted, and through the trees I could see the slope of a field of stubble corn. A congregation of crows was busy among the rows. "My home town isn't far from here," Wood said. "It wouldn't be more than thirty miles for one of those crows. Sikeston, Missouri—my daddy was a cotton farmer there. I never meant to go on the river. I guess I'd have to call it just an accident. But once I got started, I was hooked. It's another kind of life. It's like one of those drugs. There ain't no future and there ain't no past. There's nothing but the river. That's the way you get to feel. But the river has been good to me. There's enough here to keep you going. You start in decking, and if you've got enough smarts you try to climb. I'd come up to the pilothouse in my off-duty hours and watch the captain. That old man made a pilot out of me. He went back to the old river days when you could chew a man out, when you could make him feel like nothing—when you could kick him all over the deck. But he wasn't that kind of man. I learned everything from him. Any man is welcome in my pilothouse. He can come up and set and talk and enjoy the scenery any time his work is done or his watch is over. But I expect him not to abuse it. He's got to behave himself. There was a time when the river was my only home. I worked nine straight months on a boat without putting foot on shore. Me and another pilot bought a towboat and went into business on our own. I didn't have no children then, and my wife travelled with me most of the time. She really rowed the boat. She could have passed my pilot's license easier than I did. I kept at it for eight years, but it was hard work, running the boat and running the business, too. So one day I sold my share to my partner and went back to working for somebody else. But I come out ahead—I come out with my house paid for, and a nice little farm down in southern Missouri, and a couple of dollars in my pocket. The best thing about it was my wife got to understand the river. So she and I, we kind of understand each other. We don't have the trouble some fellas have. I wake up when I'm home at about 3 A.M.—I can't sleep no more. And my wife gets up and puts on that little housecoat and makes up a cup of coffee. The only thing she grumbles about is when I've got to have that little nap in the afternoon."

"My old lady won't let me sleep," the deckhand said. "When I'm at home, we don't do nothing but go."

"Yeah?" Wood said. "I don't even go to church no more. That preacher we got, he's always stopping me and telling me I have to come to church. I told him no sir. People think you're isolated here on the river. They mean isolated from the world, and that's true. But you're not isolated from yourself. You get close to yourself, you get to know your thoughts. I told that preacher, 'If you believe in a Supreme Being—and I do—you're closer to Him out here than in any old Baptist church.' The preacher don't bother me. I know what my own mind tells me. I don't have to have somebody tell me if I'm doing wrong. I'm a grown man. I know right and I know wrong, and I know it all by myself."

The cook on the National Gateway was a thin, stern, bald-headed man from Texas named W. B. Wimberly. He was a country cook, and the galley was a big room with the feel of a country kitchen. There was always a view through a double door that gave on the low main deck—a framed and changeless view of a slowly passing countryside: the lift of a grass-grown levee, a skiff pulled up on a mudbank, willow thicket and cottonwood grove, cattle grazing in a field. There was a big refrigerator, never locked, with iced tea and milk, with grapefruit juice and orange juice and tomato juice, with cold meat and cottage cheese and a bowl of hard-boiled eggs. There was a big table set for eight in the middle of the room with a crowded tray of condiments. All the usual things were there (ketchup, mustard, French dressing, chili sauce, peanut butter, steak sauce, jelly, honey), but there were also other delicacies—Frank's Red Hot Sauce, Bruce's Banana Peppers, Evangeline Gumbo Filé. I went down to dinner that day with the chief engineer, the technician Blackford, three deckhands, and the pilot, a gray, quiet Louisianan of fifty named Pierre Bourgeois. We helped ourselves from the stove and a buffet counter. Nobody talked and everybody ate. I watched one of the deckhands eat a bowl of chicken fricassee, an inch-thick slab of pot roast, mashed potatoes and gravy, lima beans (spiced with Frank's Red Hot Sauce), carrots, spinach, two wedges of corn bread, combination salad, and a dish of butterscotch pudding. There was a bowl of hard-boiled eggs on the table. He ate one egg with his chicken fricassee and two more with his pot roast, and he washed it all down with two glasses of cherry Kool-Aid. Wimberly sat in a corner and smoked and turned the pages of the *National Insider* ("How Jackie Lives When Nobody Is Looking") and sternly watched us eat.

We finished and made way for the forward watch. The engineer went back to the engine room, Blackford went out on the tow to check the refrigeration, the deckhands went off to sand and paint the texas deck. Bourgeois went up to the pilothouse, and a few minutes later I joined him there. He reached under the console and handed me a big, floppy copy of "Flood Control and Navigation Maps of the Mississippi River: Cairo, Illinois, to the Gulf of Mexico." "This river is famous for its crazy bends," he said, "and the one we're coming to is just about the craziest. See where it's marked Kentucky Point on the chart—where the river goes into a horseshoe bend that takes a big nipple out of the Missouri side. That's the bend we're coming into now. That's the famous New Madrid Bend. This is where they had that earthquake back in the Daniel Boone days— back there in 1811 and 1812. They tell me the New Madrid earthquake was the worst we ever had in this country. The river turned red and twisted around and ran upstream. It made the famous Reelfoot Lake, over there in Tennessee, and it made this New Madrid Bend. It's a real mixup. Our left bank right now is Tennessee and the right bank is Missouri, but up ahead about a mile the left bank is Kentucky again. It's nineteen miles from where we are, just coming into the bend, to where we come out, but if I was to drop you off at the neck up there you could walk across to the other end in probably fifteen minutes. It ain't much more than a mile. Some people say why don't they make a cutoff, dig a canal across the neck, save a lot of time? I say they better not. They better not fool around with any of these bends. The bends make the pressure that keeps the water level up. If you dug a straight channel from here on down to the Gulf, you wouldn't have nothing but a ditch. The water would run right off, like water off a rock. The only thing I've got against these bends is that's where you meet the traffic. I know of two tows right now that are coming up this bend. It's like they *like* to bunch up."

Bourgeois reached for the telephone, and I reopened "Flood Control and Navigation Maps of the Mississippi River." I looked again at Kentucky Point and its transplanted piece of Kentucky, and then leafed on through the book. Kentucky Point was only one among many such geographical confusions. The turnings and re-turnings of the Lower River have undone boundary lines all the way down to the Gulf. Part of Tipton County, Tennessee, now finds itself on the Arkansas side of the river, and part of Mississippi County, Arkansas, is on the Tennessee side. Part of Tunica County, Mississippi, is embedded in Lee County, Arkansas, and a good part of Lee County is over in Tunica County. Part of East Carroll Parish, Louisiana, has shifted across to Mississippi, and there is much of Mississippi isolated here and there along the Louisiana shore. I thought of Mark Twain's account of this phenomenon in "Life on the Mississippi." "The town of Delta," he reported, "used to be three miles below Vicksburg: a recent cut-off has radically changed the position, and Delta is now *two miles above* Vicksburg." I found Delta (Louisiana) on my map. It is now—almost a hundred years later—neither above nor below Vicksburg. It is directly across the river from that city, and two full miles to the west.

It was long after dark when we came into the harbor at Memphis. We took on supplies and mail from another floating ship chandlery, and Bourgeois went ashore to fly home for his fifteen days of leave. He was replaced by another Louisianan, a man named William Reeves. But I slept through all this and first heard about it from Wood the next morning, after breakfast. "Only that ain't what we call it," he said. "We don't call Memphis by its name. We call it Big Shelby. Shelby is the name of the county it's in. I don't know what the reason is. It probably goes way back to the very early days. There's a lot of traditions like that on the river. There's a crossing down near Battle Axe Bend that the chart calls Bordeaux Crossing. But what we call it on the river is Boodrow Crossing. And coming into Baton Rouge there's a point named Free Nigger Point. That's always been the name, and it don't mean nothing at all. It's just a name. But last year they changed it on the map to Free Negro Point. That made me kind of laugh. It made me think of our church back home. It was built back in my granddaddy's time. He was the town doctor and also the Baptist preacher, and he got the church built cheap out of slabs from that little sawmill they had. So everybody called it Slab Shanty Church. Then back when I was growing up—back in the nineteen-forties—the congregation raised some money and built a nice big new brick church. They named it the Union Grove Baptist Church. But you know what everybody calls it? Even the preacher? They call it Slab Shanty Church."

I went out on the tow that afternoon with Blackford. Unescorted

idlers are not permitted on red-flag barges, and I went with his permis-
sion and equipped (as regulations require) with a life jacket. We
walked along the echoing metal decks between the high-humped anhydrous-ammonia tanks. "It's easy enough to explain," he said. "All
you got to do is maintain the temperature in the tanks at minus
twenty-eight degrees. That keeps the ammonia liquid and under control. When the temperature rises, it begins to vaporize. We run the
vapor through the refrigeration unit and it liquefies again. I like this
kind of work, and I like it on the river. I like those fifteen days on
shore, too. I don't have a family. But I like to get cleaned up and
move into a motel and go partying around St. Louis. But by the
time my leave is over, I'm just about ready to come back. I'm like
homesick for the river." Blackford left me at the head of the tow.
He turned back to check his refrigeration units, and I sat down in
the sun below a drooping company beaver flag and watched the river
spreading and bending on ahead. And the traffic. There was a tow
approaching now at almost every bend. We passed the Sebring (on
two whistles) with four oil and chemical barges. We passed the Sarah
Jane (two whistles) with nine hopper barges. We passed the William
Barnes (one whistle) with ten petroleum barges. We passed the Ole
Miss (two whistles) with twenty hopper barges. We passed the Franklin Pierce (one whistle) with four petroleum barges and five jumbo
hoppers. The sunlight began to dim. There were clouds building
up to the west and south. Blackford came up and sat down and
smoked a cigarette and carefully ground it out, and then we walked
back to the boat. The clouds had gathered overhead, and the river
looked dark and heavy. The banks looked far away.

We were eating supper when the rain began. It was almost dark,
and the air was very still. It was a thin, drifting, drizzly rain, and it
hung in the air like mist. "That was the forecast," Wood said. "There's
some kind of a depression down in the Gulf. But there aren't many
pilots that enjoy a rainy night on the river. Rain makes everything
hard. If it's bad, it knocks the radar out, and if there's a lot of
wind, it's worse. It kicks up a chop so you can't hardly see the buoys.
It's almost as bad as fog."

"You ever been up there on the Ohio, Cap?" one of the deckhands
said. "Where they got that Haunted Hollow Point? They say you're

coming along on a bad ıght and you'll see the running lights of a
boat. But you get just so close and they disappear on you."

"Yeah?" Wood said. "Well, if that ever happened to me, I'd give
him a whistle and plenty of room. I wouldn't take no chances on
him being a ghost."

The rain dripped down all night, and it was drizzling at breakfast
on Thursday morning. But we were still moving. We were due in
Baton Rouge sometime that night, and we were more or less on
schedule. Then, around eleven o'clock, the drizzle stiffened into rain,
and the wind began to blow. The rain drummed down on the open
decks and blew in at the windows in sheets. I was watching it from
the bench in the pilothouse just after dinner when a message came
over the radio from the company office in St. Louis: "Attention,
National Gateway. There is a storm moving into Louisiana from
the Gulf. We do not want you to go past Natchez. Do not go past
Natchez until further notice. Repeat. Stop at Natchez."

The relief captain, Reeves, was at the console. He was a big man
in his middle fifties, with a big belly and a big, rough, smiling face.
He acknowledged the order in a slow, untroubled voice. He hung
up and reached for a cigarette. "You hear that?" he said. "Well, I
was just thinking the same myself. I didn't think this was any ordinary
squall. I thought it looked kind of bad. But I know a good place to
tie up at Natchez. That is, if somebody else ain't already beat me
to it. And if I don't stub my toe getting there. I don't know. Look
at that son of a bitch out there—that's what I call choppy water.
We passed a tow just before you come up here that said they'd
had some trouble down around Rifle Point, and that's exactly where
we're coming to right now. I don't know if we're even going to
make it. Just look at that rain. I can't hardly see a goddam thing.
Look at them buoys, the way they're jumping around. You can't
tell red from black. Well, I know one thing—I'm sure as hell not
going down through Natchez. I sure don't want to run that bridge
down there today. The place I got in mind is at the upper end of
town. It's on the Louisiana side. But what if somebody's got it? I
sure don't see no traffic. And there's a fella tied up over there. It
looks like everybody is already tied up but us."

Reeves put out his cigarette. He picked up the binoculars and
gazed out through the streaming glass. He put the binoculars down

and lighted another cigarette. "Well, it won't be long now," he said. "That's Magnolia Bluff beginning over there. That's where those kids found all that money that time. They were playing along the shore and they saw something laying in the water and they fished it out and it was a coffee can full of silver dimes. Son of a bitch— you know what I think? I think I'd better start looking right now for a tree to tie up to. I got a feeling my place is took. I don't see a tree that will hold me. I don't see no trees at all. I don't see nothing but willow sprouts. And I sure wouldn't lay up like that fella over there at that towhead. He'll have some trouble getting off. But it ain't as bad as it was. See how that bluff has cut off the wind. But I don't know. There just ain't no real trees. And—son of a bitch. What did I tell you? There's my place and there's a fella in it. You know something? I'm going to have to try and run that goddam bridge."

I stood up for a better view. An old brick building appeared low down on the Mississippi shore. A street climbed up the bluff behind it. There were rooftops showing along the top of the bluff. That was Natchez. We came around a bend. A bridge loomed up through the rain. The channel markers led between two middle piers. The gap didn't look much wider than our tow. But Reeves didn't head for the channel. He pulled the head of the tow far off to the left, angling toward the Natchez shore, running straight at a string of barges moored along the face of a wharf. The bridge widened and rose higher overhead. An orange trailer truck was moving slowly across the bridge in the driving, blinding rain. Then the string of moored barges began to swing away—swing off to the left, and suddenly out of sight behind the big stone face of a pier—and we were back in the channel and sliding under the bridge and plunging out on the other side.

"Son of a bitch," Reeves said. He reached for another cigarette. "We made it. We got through there real fine. But I have to thank that Natchez bluff. I'd never made it with that wind hitting me. But goddam it—I still got to find me a place to park. I can't keep rolling along half blind like this. But I don't know. Everywhere I see a likely-looking tree there's a fella already tied up to it. No, sir. I ain't never had this kind of trouble trying to find a place to tie up. There's nothing on this left bank—nothing open, anyway. I won-

der should I go over there to the right bank and take a look? I
sure can't see from here. Maybe if I got real close— But I can't.
It's too shallow. See that black buoy. It's all of it shoal over there.
There's nothing to do but keep going. I never saw anything like
this in my whole damn life. Every tree got a barge tied to it. And
where there ain't any barges there's nothing but levee bank. I don't
know where we're going. I don't know what we're going to do. And
we got a fifty-mile wind coming at us. Look at them trees, how
they're bending. I swear to God, I just don't know. They told me
stop at Natchez, and here we are still going. Goddam—there's De-
struction Landing over yonder, and that's St. Catherine Bend just
ahead. We're way below Natchez. We're fifteen miles below. I got
to do something soon. I think I'll try right now. I sure would hate
to have this tow bust up. What I'm going to do is go into that
right bank there. I don't think much of the trees, but it's deep enough,
and it even looks like it might be a little bit slack. I do believe I've
found me a place. I do believe I have." He picked up the intercom
microphone. "Angelo? Frank? All right, fellas—let's go."

We moved into a right-hand crossing, back toward Louisiana. The
only visible buoy was a red buoy a hundred yards or so from shore.
Beyond it was a kind of cove, a little indentation in a bank of crumbling
mud, and above the bank was a grove of tall, feathery willows. The
trees were thrashing, bending almost double. Three deckhands in
hooded yellow slickers came humping out on the main deck down
below. They ducked across the deck, heads down and slickers flapping,
and up a ladder to the stern of the starboard ammonia barge, and
on to a coil of heavy mooring line. The sound of the engines changed
to the vibrating roar of reverse. Reeves was standing now, leaning
across the console, peering. We slid—every deck and bulkhead clang-
ing against the wind and the current—half broadside into the bank.
The deckhands ran out a wooden gangplank. They went down the
plank, hauling the line, and into the mud and up the bank to the
trees. The trees leaned flat in a wilder gust, and two of them splintered
and broke. The feathery top of one lifted high in the air. It sailed
away like a gull. The deckhands struggled back aboard and broke
out another line. The engines turned gently over in a slow, braking
reverse. The rain came down and the mudbank melted and crumbled
and the willows thrashed in the wind. But we were out of it now.

We were out of the current, out of the pull of the river, sitting safe on a sheltered shore. Reeves turned away from the console. He walked back to the stove and picked up the coffeepot. "I'm going to have some coffee," he said. "How about you?"

The storm was almost over by the time I went down to bed that night. The rain had ended and the wind had dropped, and I could see the new moon racing through the last of the clouds and the deep-blue sky opening up beyond. But the river still looked and sounded rough, and we were still moored along the mudbank. I lay in the dark and listened to the river and the sound of the engines still clanking away in reverse. A voice in the passageway said, "Five feet on the gauge at St. Louis." I dozed, and suddenly awoke. It was still dark—I had dozed for only a moment—but the engines had a different sound. I sat up and looked out the window. The mudbank was gone. We were well out on the river, and moving. I was in no hurry to get to Baton Rouge. But life on the river is movement, and it was good to be moving again. I rolled over and went back to sleep.

# First Boat to King Island

The Eskimos were waiting for us on the beach just beyond the boulder breakwater on the eastern outskirts of Nome. It was six o'clock in the evening, but the June sun was still high in the sky and the air was almost warm. Offshore a mile or two, the ice that had moved out in the night was white and clear on the horizon. We said goodbye to the friend who had driven us out from town, and unloaded our gear—boxes of food, seabags, sleeping bags, a portable Coleman stove, some photographic equipment—and carried it across the road and down the embankment and onto the beach. The beach was steep and stony, with dirty snow in the hollows and a heavy crust of ice at the edge of the water. The *umiak* was moored to the ice. It was an open dory made of walrus hide stretched over a wooden frame, and it looked to be about thirty feet long. The Eskimos—three men, three women, and three teen-age boys—were loading the boat from a pile of boxes and bundles and gasoline tins and oil drums and oars and ice lances and boat hooks and rifles. I counted a dozen rifles in the pile, and there were others already stacked in the bow of the boat. The Eskimos were King Island Eskimos. Their native place was a little island in the Bering Sea about a hundred miles northwest of Nome. They had spent the winter in Nome, and now that the ice was breaking up they were going back to King Island to take supplies to their friends and relatives there, to hunt for seal and walrus, and to collect for sale on the mainland the walrus-ivory carvings that the islanders had made during the winter. My companions—John Fuller, a teacher in a school for Eskimo children run by the Bureau of Indian Affairs, and Joseph Rychetnik, an outdoor photographer and a former Alaska state trooper—and I had arranged to go with them. Their boat would be the first to visit King Island since the ice had closed in last fall.

The Eskimos watched us coming down the beach. Some of them smiled, and one of the men waved. They all wore parkas with the hoods thrown back and dungarees, and most of them wore sealskin mukluk boots. The women wore flowered-cotton Mother Hubbards over their parkas. Two of the women, two of the boys, and one of the men wore glasses. The man who had waved came up to meet us. He was the boat captain, and his name was Vincent Kunnuk.

"No more to do," he said. "Everything is ready. We only wait for the old man."

Fuller nodded. He seemed to know what Kunnuk meant.

Kunnuk looked at me. "The old man has the experience," he said. "There is always an old man on a boat. He knows the weather and everything about the ice."

"I'm glad to hear it," Rychetnik said. "I made one patrol to King Island when I was on the police, and I got stuck there for over a week."

"I wonder if I know the old man," Fuller said.

"May be," Kunnuk said. "He is Pikonganna—Aloysius Pikonganna."

"Aloysius, eh?" Fuller said. "Good. Real good."

Kunnuk went back to the boat. We followed him down with our gear, and he showed us where to stow it. The boat was powered by two outboard motors—one at the stern and the other hung in a well a few feet forward. Two motors were no more than enough. They would have a lot of weight to move. The boat held nothing yet except gear, but it already sat low in the water. There wasn't much more than a foot of freeboard left.

A car stopped up on the road. The door opened and a little man on crutches got out. He had a rifle slung across his back. He called out something in Eskimo—a string of purrs and a sudden bark—

and laughed and swung himself down the embankment.

"Now we go," Kunnuk said. "The old man is here. He goes on crutches all his life, but it makes no difference. He does everything a man can do."

The sea was a deep, translucent green and as flat as a village pond. We moved slowly away from the beach with only the stern motor working. Kunnuk sat at the helm. He kept the motor throttled down until we were clear of the shoals and shallows along the shore. Then he nodded to the man at the well, and the second motor coughed and stuttered and came alive, and the shore began to slide away. I watched the beach flatten out and the tumbledown houses across the road shrink down behind the embankment and the big brown mountainous hills rise up in the distance. Snow still lay on the tops of the hills and in their sheltered folds. The boat cut heavily away to the right, heading generally west, between the shore and the ice floes out to sea. I felt a breath of cooler air.

Aloysius Pikonganna sat in the bow on a plank laid across the gunwales. He had a pair of binoculars on a strap around his neck and a toothpick between his teeth. Below him, huddled in the shelter of a canvas windbreak, were the three women and the youngest boy. The boy wore a little pale-blue souvenir fedora, and on the front of the crown was a crayon scribble: "I want to hold your hand." The other boys were packed in the stern with Kunnuk and the other men. Fuller, Rychetnik, and I sat amidships with the jumble of gear. I had a few inches of thwart to sit on and the iron curve of a fifty-gallon oil drum to rest my back against. Fuller was perched on the corner of an open box of pots and pans, and Rychetnik was sunk among his photographic equipment. But we were thickly padded with clothes. Rychetnik and I had on Bean hunting boots and two pairs of socks and Air Force survival pants and Eddie Bauer down-lined jackets over two heavy shirts and thermal underwear. Fuller wore an Eskimo uniform—fur parka, fur pants, and mukluk boots. He shifted on his box, and looked at me.

"Comfortable?" he asked.

"I'm fine," I said.

"I hope so," he said. "We've got at least fourteen hours of this ahead of us, you know."

"How about you?" I said.

"I'm O.K.," he said. "Besides, I'm used to it. This is just the way these cats are. They've always got room for one more."

"Just relax and enjoy it," Rychetnik said. "Be like me."

Pikonganna looked over his shoulder and raised a warning hand. There were ice floes in the sea ahead. The boat slowed down. Kunnuk stood up in the stern with his hand on the tiller and watched the drifting ice. Some of the floes were eight or ten feet in diameter, and some were twenty or thirty or fifty or more. All of them were four or five feet thick, but their edges were deeply undercut and they all were raddled with pools and puddles. We picked our way among them. A file of big black-and-white eider ducks came over the horizon. I watched them beating slowly along just clear of the water—and a dark shape moved on a floe far off to the left. It could only be a seal. One of the Eskimos let out a yell and grabbed up a rifle. But the seal was already gone. The Eskimo laughed and pulled the trigger anyway. The bullet whined away across the ice.

We came out from among the drifting floes and into a stretch of green open water. The boat began to move again. But after about ten minutes Pikonganna held up his hand again. There was more ice ahead. Everything in front of us was ice. The sea was a plain of shifting floes for as far as I could see. Kunnuk cut the motors, and we drifted up to the flank of one of the big floes. One of the men took a lance and chipped away the treacherous overhang and then jumped out on the floe. Pikonganna tossed him a line, and he stuck his lance in the ice and knotted the line around it. Another Eskimo followed him and secured the stern of the boat with another line and lance. Kunnuk came forward.

"Now we wait," he said. "But the ice is moving. It will open up pretty soon." He stepped on the gunwale and onto the ice. "The women will make us some tea."

The women were already at work. They uncovered a Coleman stove and handed it out and set it up on the ice not far from the boat. While two of them got the stove started, the other woman got a teakettle and went off across the floe to a pool of melted ice. Rychetnik and Fuller and I stood on the ice, stamping the circulation back into our feet, and watched her fill the kettle from the pool.

"Do they make tea out of that?" I asked.

"Relax," Rychetnik said. "Saltwater ice isn't salty. The salt is expelled when salt water freezes. That's good water in that pool. I mean, it's fresh."

"It's potable," Fuller said. "Let's take a look at the ice. But be careful where you step. This rotten ice is full of potholes."

We walked down the floe. The ice was plainly moving. There was a lead of open water just ahead, and I could see that it was getting wider. The farther floe was pulling away in the grip of the tide. But the lead was still far from wide enough. I looked at my watch. It was twenty minutes past nine. Though the brightness had gone out of the sky, it was still full light. Everything was still fully visible—the hills and mountains on the mainland, a bread-loaf island in the distance, the drifting floes through which we had come. But the sun had moved down behind the mountains in the north, and it was only there that the sky had color. Overhead, it was dirty white, like a snowstorm sky, and the sky on the southern horizon was a cold, slaty blue. The mountains stood against a glory of pink and green and yellow.

When we got back to the boat, the Eskimos were gathered around a tarpaulin in front of the stove. The tarpaulin was spread with food— a box of pilot crackers, a tin of butter, and a big square of whale blubber. The blubber looked like a block of cheese—pale pink cheese with a thick black rind. We stopped at the boat and got a bag of sandwiches out of one of our boxes, and then joined the circle of Eskimos.

"It's moving, Vince," Fuller said. "It's opening up over there real fast."

"I know," Kunnuk said, and took a swallow of tea. "But we wait awhile. Have some tea." He spoke to the women in Eskimo, and picked up a fan-shaped knife with an ivory grip and cut off a slice of blubber. "Have some *muktuk?*"

Rychetnik smiled and shook his head.

"No, thanks, Vince," Fuller said. "Not right now."

Kunnuk laughed and looked at me. "This is the best *muktuk*— from the bullhead whale. Black *muktuk.*"

I took the slice of *muktuk*. I sat down on the ice, and one of the women passed me a plastic cup of dark, steaming tea. I looked at the *muktuk*. The blubber didn't look like fat. It had a softer, more gelatinous look. I took a bite of it. It was very tender and almost tasteless. The only flavor was a very faint sweetness. There was one more bite of *muktuk* left. I ate it and washed it down with a gulp of tea. Then I opened my sandwich.

It was almost eleven o'clock when we finally left the floe. The sky was still bright pink behind the mountains. We moved along a crooked lead of open water on one throttled-down motor. The floe on the left was piled with shattered slabs of pressure ice, sometimes to a height of four or five feet. Every now and then, the ice would give a kind of moan, and a big slab would slide into the water and the boat would lurch. Two of the Eskimos stood at the gunwales with lances and pushed the floating ice away. Pikonganna was standing at his lookout post. He looked at his watch, and turned and said something to one of the women. She reached under a pile of quilts and brought out a little plastic radio. It came alive with a thunder of Russian. Then a screech of static. Then a voice said, ". . . and partly cloudy tonight with widely scattered showers. Cloudy tomorrow. The present temperature in Nome is forty-two degrees." There was a moment of whistling silence, and then came the sound of guitars and a sob of Hawaiian music. The woman turned the radio off.

The lead began to broaden, and we were back in open water. The only big expanse of ice in sight was a shelf of anchored ice that stretched between the mainland and the distant bread-loaf island. Kunnuk came forward across the gear. He stepped over us and over the women and joined Pikonganna at the bow. They talked softly together for a couple of minutes. Then Kunnuk laughed and started back. He stopped where we sat, and balanced himself on the gunwale.

"The old man says we go around Sledge Island," he said. That was the bread-loaf island in the distance. "But after that—no sweat. No more ice."

I came out of a dull, uncomfortable doze. I was hunched against the flank of the oil drum, and I was stiff and cramped and cold. I sat up—and there was Sledge Island. It loomed hugely up no more than three hundred yards off the bow. There was a fringe of ice, a field of soggy snow, a rubble of boulders, and a brown grassy slope rising steeply to a brown grassy summit. My watch said five minutes to two. The sun was up from behind the mountains, but the sky was gray with cloud. We seemed to be making directly for the island. I looked at Fuller. Rychetnik was asleep face down between a seabag and a metal camera case, but Fuller was awake. He was sitting under the spread of his big parka hood, smoking a pipe.

"It looks like we're going to land," I said.

Fuller took the pipe out of his mouth. "Boat trouble," he said. "Vince says there's something wrong with one of the motors. He wants to stop and take a look at it."

Rychetnik sat up as we scraped alongside the shelf of anchored ice. "Hey," he said. "Where are we?"

"Sledge Island," I said.

"Sledge Island?" he said. "We're only at Sledge Island?"

"Relax," I said. "Relax and enjoy it."

When the boat was made fast, Kunnuk and one of the other men lifted the motor out of the well and began to take it apart. The trouble seemed to be in the feed line. I watched them for a minute. Then I followed the others through the field of snow to a ledge among the boulders, where the women had set up their stove. I sat down on a rock and gazed at them. They were boiling down snow for tea. I felt more than tired. I felt disoriented. The midnight daylight was confusing. After my sleep, it should have been morning. It gave me a very strange feeling.

Rychetnik touched me on the arm.

"Let's take our tea down the line a ways," he said. "Jack and I think it's time for a little depressant."

The idea of a drink at half past two in the morning was no stranger than anything else. I got up, and we sloshed through the snow to the sheltering lee of a boulder. Rychetnik handed each of us a little two-ounce bottle of Scotch, and we emptied them into our tea.

"It's better not to drink in front of the Eskimos," Rychetnik said. "It doesn't seem right unless you're going to pass the bottle around. And this is no place to do that."

"Good God, no," Fuller said. "I've lived and worked with Eskimos for quite a few years. As a matter of fact, I'm a first sergeant in the Eskimo Scouts. I know them and I love them. I really love them. Those cats have to have something to survive in this environment, and they've got it. They've got every virtue. They're honest—they're completely honest—and they're loyal and they're generous and they're brave and they're always in good spirits. Nothing bothers them. But they can't drink. When they do, they get drunk. And when they get drunk, they go wild—they go absolutely wild."

We left Sledge Island with both motors working. I settled back in my oil-drum seat and listened to their steady, synchronized growl. The sea beyond the island was all open water. The only ice was off to the north, along the mainland shore. But the weather had also changed. The overcast was heavier now, and the breeze had sharpened, and the sea had faded from green to gray. I felt a drop of rain.

One of the women turned and caught my eye and smiled. She pointed toward the shore, and held up four fingers.

"Four years ago, we stay there one week," she said. "Bad weather. Then we stay three days at Sledge Island. More bad weather." She smiled again. "Was very bad trip."

"It sounds bad," I said.

She pointed again toward the shore. "Is called Pinguk," she said, and turned away.

I felt more drops of rain. There was a raincoat with a hood in my seabag. I felt around and found it and put it on and tied the hood under my chin. In the pocket was a pair of wool-lined rubber gloves, and I put them on, too. The rain burst into a spitting shower and then sank down to a long, cold drizzle. Rychetnik was asleep and snoring among his photographic gear, and Fuller sat humped on his box. Pikonganna stood on watch at the bow in a shiny translucent raincoat made of walrus intestines. I pulled up my legs and turned on my side and tried to fit myself against the curve of the oil drum. It wasn't very comfortable, but I was out of the wind and warm and dry. The last thing I remember was the rattle of the rain on my raincoat hood.

The boat was reeling and rolling, and it lurched me wide awake. It was almost six o'clock. I sat up and hung on to the thwart. We were rolling in a heavy chop. Rychetnik was also sitting up. He sat with one hand on the gunwale, bracing himself. It was still raining, and everything looked strangely dark. But is wasn't the darkness of night. Then I realized—it was fog. The boat gave a sickening roll. We were running broadside to the wind and wallowing in the trough of the waves. Rychetnik looked at me and smiled and shook his head.

"This is getting kind of hairy," he said.

"What's the matter?" I said.

"Aloysius says it's too rough to go on," he said. "Too rough and too foggy. We're turning around and heading in to shore."

Fuller leaned over my shoulder. "Too rough and too foggy and only one motor," he said. "That motor conked out again."

"I wonder where we are," I said.

Fuller shrugged. "I don't know," he said. "My guess is somewhere off Cape Woolley."

"Where is that?" I said.

"Nowhere," he said. "It's just a name on the map."

"I know Cape Woolley," Rychetnik said. "I was up along there on my first assignment as a trooper. It was right around this time of year, too. I flew up from Nome with a bush pilot. As a matter of fact, it was Gene Farland. Three Eskimos had got drunk in Nome and gone out fishing in a skin boat and never came back. My job was to try to find them. Somebody said they had headed up this coast, so we took off. We flew along just above the beach—and pretty soon there was the boat. It was hanging up there in the driftwood. Then, a little farther on, we found the bodies. They weren't ten feet apart."

"What happened?" I said.

"There was a storm and they were drunk and the boat capsized and they went into the water," he said. "This is the Bering Sea. When you go into the water up here, that's the end of the story. You've had it."

"I don't know whether you've noticed," Fuller said, "but there aren't any life preservers on this boat."

The boat began to come around. It rocked and slipped and lumbered into the wind. Now that we were out of the trough, the heavy rolling stopped, and the boat sat a little steadier, but the head wind held us down to a bumpy crawl. We bumped through the chop for about an hour. It was a queer, empty twilit hour. There was nothing to see but the boat and the blowing rain and a few hundred feet of wild gray water vanishing into fog. It gave me an uneasy feeling. It was frightening to think that only half an inch of walrus hide lay between us and the clutch of that glacial water. But I was too tired and cramped and cold to really think about it.

A sheet of white ice emerged from the fog. It was shore ice anchored to a point of land. We moved along the flank of the ice, and the fog began to thin. The wind was blowing in offshore gusts, and it tore the thinning fog away in sudden streaks and patches. Land appeared beyond the ice. There was a narrow beach piled high with driftwood, a low embankment, and then a misty reach of tundra. A rhythmic whistling sounded overhead. I twisted my head and looked. It was a string of twenty or thirty big, dark-headed ducks swinging out to sea. Their size and the whistling made them goldeneyes. They dropped and braked and settled down on the water.

Kunnuk and Pikonganna exchanged a couple of shouts, and we edged closer in to shore. The shore ice shelf was deeply undercut, and its surface was ravaged with cracks and potholes. But apparently it would do—or would have to do. We came alongside, lifting and falling in the chop, and two of the men leaned out and hacked away the flimsy overhang. Another man and one of the boys jumped out on the ice and held the boat fast with lines. Kunnuk came forward. His eyes were red, and his face looked drawn.

"Everybody out," he said. "This ice is no good. The old man says is too rotten to hold the boat. So we unload quick and get the boat up on the beach."

The man and the boy continued to hold the boat. The rest of us worked on the gear. We hauled the boxes and the bags and the cases and the rifles and the tins and the drums and the motors well up from the edge of the ice and covered them with some strips of tarpaulin. Then we went back to the boat and got a handhold on the bowline and dug in our heels. One of the women let out a wailing heave-ho yell, and we heaved. The bow of the boat lifted and hung, and then slid up on the ice. We braced ourselves, and the woman yelled again: "Hooooo-*huke!*" We heaved again. One of the Eskimos stepped through a pothole up to his thigh, and I slipped and sat down hard on the ice, but the boat came up another five or six feet. Another heave brought all but the stern of it clear of the water, and after that it was easier. With some of us pulling and the rest pushing, the boat slid over the soggy ice like a sled. There was no need now for the women to help. They got their stove and some other supplies and then went on across the ice and up the beach to the tundra. By the time we got there with the boat, the women had collected a supply of driftwood branches and logs, and even trees, and had a big fire going. We careened the boat a few feet from the fire and propped it up on its side with the oars and boat hooks. It made an excellent windbreak and a kind of shelter from the rain.

We stood around the fire and warmed ourselves and caught our breath. The wind tore at the fire, and the flames leaped and twisted and darted in all directions, and my face was scorched but my feet stayed cold. It was a hot and furious fire. It took a lot of driftwood to keep it going, and the wood that the women had collected went fast. It was the deadest driftwood I had ever seen. Years of weathering on this desert beach had dried it to papery husks, and it burned almost like paper. When the woodpile was down to a few sticks and branches, Rychetnik and I volunteered to bring in another supply. It was plentiful enough. There was driftwood heaped head high at the high-water mark along the beach as far as I could see. It must have been accumulating there forever. We made a dozen trips and brought back a dozen logs—big, barkless silver-gray logs that weighed practically nothing. As we dropped our last load, Fuller came struggling up from the ice with a box and a bag of perishables. The women had their stove set up, and they were making tea and boiling a pot of mush. Rychetnik looked at them and then at his watch.

"Hey," he said. "It's eight o'clock. What are *we* going to do about breakfast?"

"Whatever you say," Fuller said. "But I didn't get any sleep last night and I'm really not too hungry."

"Neither am I," I said.

"Besides," Fuller said, "I'm not real eager to break out the stove right now and do a lot of cooking and washing up and getting packed again. It wouldn't be worth the trouble. My guess is this weather is going to clear, and I know these cats. They'll be wanting to take right off."

"But what about breakfast?" Rychetnik said.

"I brought up the rest of the sandwiches," Fuller said. "And we've got some cans of chocolate milk."

Fuller was right about the weather. The rain had stopped by the time we finished breakfast, and the clouds were breaking up. There were patches of bright sky overhead, and the air was bright and clear. Even the wind had dropped. It looked like a beautiful day, but we wouldn't be leaving soon. The sea was still running high and white. Fuller dragged himself away from the fire and lay down in the shelter of the boat. Almost at once, he was snoring. I was tired, but the change in the weather made me restless. Rychetnik was engrossed in his cameras. I got up and walked around the boat and out onto the tundra.

The tundra stretched endlessly away to the north and south, and far to the east, a smoky gray on the blue horizon, were mountains. It was an enormous, empty plain. There were no trees, no bushes, no grass. There were only weedy hummocks and pockets of bog and trickling, ice-water brooks. Some of the hollows were still drifted over with snow. I skirted a bog and stepped over a brook, and a bird flew up from almost under my foot. It was followed by another. They were tawny, long-billed birds—snipe. A few minutes later, I flushed a phalarope. The tundra wasn't as empty as it looked. There were shrieks and whistles and drumming wings at almost every step I took. I flushed more snipe and phalaropes, and also sandpipers and plovers and ptarmigan. The ptarmigan had a shabby look. Their plumage was still a confusion of winter white and summer brown. Once, in the distance, I saw a flight of sandhill cranes, and there were many strings of ducks and geese. The geese were mostly snow geese, but there were also emperor geese and brant. The sun came suddenly out. It blazed down like tropical sun. I unfastened my padded jacket, and then took it off. It was actually hot. I sat down on a hummock and folded my jacket into a pillow and lay back. The hummock was matted with lingenberry vines and tiny creeping willow, and it made a soft and springy bed. I closed my eyes and enjoyed the feel of the sun on my face.

I woke up cold and shivering. The sun was gone and the fog was back, and it took me a moment to remember where I was. I put on my jacket and started back to the camp. My head was still thick with sleep. I stopped at a brook and squatted down and splashed some water on my face. That finished waking me up. I went on, stepping and stretching and hopping from hummock to hummock. The fog made everything seem very still. The mountains had disappeared in the fog, but I could see the camp across the tundra. A small white tent now stood not far from the driftwood fire. Several men were gathered at the bow of the upturned boat. One of them was Rychetnik. I waved, and he came out to meet me. He was grinning.

"We'll never get off this beach," he said.

"Not with this fog," I said.

"I don't mean only the weather," he said.

"Now what?" I said.

"More boat trouble," he said. "One of the Eskimos was sacked out under the boat, and he happened to look up—and what do you think he saw?"

"What?" I said.

"Daylight," he said. "There was a hole in the bottom of the boat about the size of a dime. Vince and Sam Mogg are patching it up. They think it probably happened when we were dragging the boat up over the driftwood."

"What about that conked-out motor?" I said.

"I think they've finally got that fixed," he said. "But don't start getting any ideas. There's something wrong with the other motor now. It needs a shear pin on the propeller shaft. They're going to fix that this afternoon."

"Do you have any more of those little bottles you had last night?" I said.

Rychetnik laughed. "No," he said. "But I've got a big one."

I followed him around the boat and around the fire and around behind the Eskimo tent. Fuller was there, sitting on a log in front of our portable stove and searching through a box of groceries. He looked refreshed by his nap, and resigned to a stay on the beach. I filled a pan with water from the nearest snow-melt brook, and Fuller found some paper cups, and Rychetnik got out a fifth of Scotch. We sat around the stove and drank our drinks. The Scotch was good with the cold snow water, and it made the fog and the beach and the miles of tundra seem less bleak. Then Fuller cooked us a lunch of bacon and eggs. It was the first hot food I had eaten in almost twenty-four hours, and nothing ever tasted any better. We finished off with bread and butter and strawberry preserves and a pot of strong boiled coffee.

We spent the afternoon hauling driftwood for the fire. The Eskimo tent had been raised for the women, and we could hear them talking and laughing inside whenever we stopped at the fire to rest and warm ourselves. We also worked to the sound of shooting. The Eskimo boys roamed up and down the beach with .22 rifles, and they shot at anything that made a target—a driftwood stump, a raft of ducks far out to sea, a flight of mile-high geese. Kunnuk sat alone in the shelter of the upturned boat with a cigarette in his mouth and filed and shaped a nail into a new shear pin. When he finished, he walked down and stood on the edge of the beach and looked at the water. The next time I came back to the fire, he was sitting there with the portable radio in his lap. I sat down beside him. We listened to a snatch of Siberian Russian and the end of a talk about getting back to the Bible. A hillbilly tenor sang "Does He Love You Like I Do?" Then a voice said: "This is radio station KICY, in Nome, Alaska. The time is six o'clock. Here is the weather forecast for Nome and vicinity: Fair and cold tonight. Fair and warmer tomorrow. The present temperature in Nome is thirty-three degrees."

Kunnuk turned off the radio. "Good weather coming," he said. "Maybe we leave soon. Maybe by midnight."

But the fog hung on. At nine o'clock, it looked thicker than ever. I doubted that we would be leaving by midnight, and I didn't care. I hardly cared if we ever left. Work and the weather and a drink of Scotch had given me a big appetite, and I had eaten a big dinner of reindeer steak, macaroni and cheese, canned peaches, cookies, and coffee. All I wanted to do was sleep. Someone would wake me before we left. If we left. I found a corner deep under the boat and took off my boots and my jacket and my heavy survival pants and unrolled my sleeping bag and crawled in. Something poked into the small of my back. There was a stick or something under my sleeping bag. I tried to squirm it away, and it moved an inch or two. That wasn't enough. I would have to climb out and move the bag. But instead I fell asleep.

I slept all night. I awoke to a crying and croaking and whistling of birds. It was half past five. There was frost on the ground, and the air was cold, but the sea looked calm, and the sun was shining in a wide blue sky. The fog was completely gone. I sat up. Kunnuk was propped on his elbow in a sleeping bag on my left.

"We make it today," he said. "Look!" He handed me a pair of

binoculars and pointed out to sea. "You can see King Island."

I looked, but I couldn't see it.

"Maybe I know better where to look," he said. "I was born there."

I got into my clothes and rolled up my sleeping bag. Underneath it was the end of one of the boat lines. I stooped out from under the boat and into the bright sunlight. Most of the others were already up. The women were boiling another big pot of mush. I washed my face in the snow-melt brook. The water felt even colder than it had the day before. It was so cold it make my nose ache. I was starting back when Rychetnik came up to get some water for breakfast, and we walked back together. The stove was going, and Fuller, in a bright-red hunting shirt, was peeling bacon into a frying pan. Then, while Rychetnik got the coffee started and I got out some cups and plates and knives and forks and spoons, he stirred up a bowl of pancake batter. He fried the pancakes in the bacon pan, and we ate them with butter and strawberry preserves.

We finished breakfast at a little after six, and a few minutes later the Eskimos began to break camp. The women did the packing. Kunnuk called us over to help the men with the boat. We rolled it back on its keel and swung it around and dragged it down and across the ice and let it into the water. The glare of the sun on the frosty ice was dazzling. Two of the boys held the boat against the edge of the ice, and we went back and got our gear. The ground where the women's tent had been was littered with bones and cigarette butts. Aloysius Pikonganna directed the loading of the boat. The arrangement was somewhat different from that at Nome. It was planned for safe and easy shooting if we happened to get a shot at a seal. Rychetnik and Fuller and I shared the forward thwart again, but the gear was all piled amidships and the women and two of the boys were also settled there. The other boy and a man called Norbert took over the motors, with Norbert doing the steering. Kunnuk and Sam Mogg joined Pikonganna in the bow with the guns. We pushed away from the shore, and I looked over the side of the boat. The water was a yellowy green and so clear that I could see the bottom, five or six feet below. The bottom was stone—big slabs of granite worn smooth by grinding ice. It was as smooth and flat and bare as a pavement.

The motors started up, first the one at the stern and then the other, and the boat began to move. The women huddled closer together. They bowed their heads and made the sign of the cross, and their lips moved silently in prayer. Then they sat back, and two of them lighted cigarettes. We left the last of the shore ice and came out into open water and into an easy swell. Yesterday's chop had gone with the fog. An acre of rafting eider ducks exploded off to the right. I watched the big birds beating slowly in to shore. The shore looked just as it had when we saw it on Thursday morning. There was no sign that anyone had ever camped there. Kunnuk turned and looked back down the boat. He was smiling, with a cigarette in his mouth, and sparks of sunlight glinted on his glasses.

"Everybody sleep good?" he said.

The women nodded and the boys grinned and Norbert yelled something in Eskimo. Everybody laughed.

"Good," Kunnuk said. "Now we got good weather. Now we travel."

Sam Mogg caught my eye.

"We got Sears, Roebuck weather," he said.

"What?" I said.

"Sears, Roebuck weather," he said. "I ordered it."

The radio came suddenly on. A familiar voice said, ". . . seven o'clock, and the present temperature in Nome is forty-four degrees. The wind is northeast at fourteen. The forecast is for fair and warmer today, tonight, and tomorrow." In spite of the sun, it was cold on the water. I could feel the forecast wind. I zipped up my jacket and put on my gloves and listened to an operatic tenor singing "I Love to Laugh." He sounded very far away. When he laughed ("Ha-ha, hee-hee"), he sounded even remoter.

King Island came faintly into sight at about eight-thirty. It was just a cloud on the western horizon. I got out a pair of binoculars and fixed them on the cloud. The cloud became a bigger and darker cloud, but it was still no more than a cloud. Then it began to grow. It darkened and broadened and lifted against the sky. By nine o'clock, the cloud was visibly an island. It continued to grow, and to change. Through the binoculars I watched it shift from a little gray lift of land to a rocky mountain rising steeply from the sea.

The woman who had spoken to me before leaned forward. She

was an elderly woman with a big, square face framed in her parka hood.

"King Island," she said. "You see?"

I nodded. "It looks like a mountain," I said.

"Ukivok is Eskimo name," she said. "Not King Island. Eskimo call it Ukivok."

"Ukivok," I said. "What does that mean in Eskimo?"

"We go up on top Ukivok," she said. "We go high up and pick green flower. Many green flower grow on top Ukivok now."

"What is green flower?" I said.

"Is good," she said. "Is like salad."

Floating ice began to appear up ahead. A flight of murre swung low across our bow, and in the distance a kittiwake soared. King Island rose higher and higher. I watched it through the binoculars. It looked to be about two miles long, and it really was a mountain. Its sides were weathered into crags and pinnacles, and they rose abruptly from a beach of anchored ice to a saddle summit that was still partly covered with snow and at least a thousand feet high. It seemed impossible that anyone could live there.

I turned to the woman behind me. "Where do the people live on Ukivok?" I said. "Where is the village?"

"Ukivok is name of village," she said. "Island and village is same name."

"Where is Ukivok village?" I said.

She smiled and shook her head. "Not this side," she said. "Too much mountain. On other side."

Fuller gave me a nudge. "Walrus," he said, and pointed off to the left.

I put up the binoculars again. I saw them almost at once—a row of six or eight enormous creatures sitting erect on an isolated floe. They were reddish brown, with big sloping shoulders and little round heads and drooping two-foot tusks. They had a prehistoric look. They also looked strangely human.

"You see them, Vince?" Fuller said.

"I see them," Kunnuk said. "Good ivory, too. But we don't hunt walrus today. No room in the boat."

The shelf of anchored ice was wider than it had looked at first.

We were still two or three miles from the island when we came in sight of its outer edge. But there were stretches of open water showing within it, and it seemed to be breaking up. Pikonganna stood balanced on his lookout plank surveying the ice. He said something to Kunnuk. Kunnuk nodded and looked back at Norbert and raised his hand in a signal. The boat cut away to the right. We moved northward along the edge of the shelf through a wash of broken floes. After ten or fifteen minutes, a break appeared in the anchored ice. We turned into a calm blue lead as broad as a boulevard.

We followed the lead for about a mile. It ran between two glittering shores of tossed and tumbled ice. Pikonganna held up his hand, and the motors slowed. There was a sudden bend just ahead. We moved slowly around the bend. Pikonganna raised his hand again, and the motors cut off. Fifty yards beyond the bend, the lead abruptly ended. We drifted up to the dead-end ice, and two of the boys jumped ashore and made the boat fast with lines and lances. Kunnuk stepped over the bow and stood and helped Pikonganna down, and Sam Mogg handed Pikonganna out his crutches. Kunnuk and Pikonganna moved off across the ice. I watched them climb to the top of a big ice ridge. They stood there studying the surrounding ice with binoculars for a moment, and then Kunnuk turned and waved.

Sam Mogg gave a grunt. "Time to eat," he said.

The women set up their stove at the foot of the ridge. They filled the teakettle with melted ice from a hollow in the floe and got out a bag of dried seal ribs. Rychetnik and Fuller and I sat down on a ledge of ice nearby and made an easy lunch of bread and butter and bologna and Swiss cheese and canned grapefruit juice and chocolate bars. From where we sat, King Island looked hardly a mile away. The cliffs that formed its northern tip loomed steeper than ever. Some of them were stained yellow with lichen, and the air around them was alive with birds. Kunnuk came down from the ridge. He stopped where we sat on his way to join the other Eskimos.

"Don't worry," he said. "We make it O.K. The old man and I see plenty other leads."

There was another blue lead about a hundred yards back down the lead we were on. It was narrow and twisting, but it led in the right direction. The King Island cliffs rose dead ahead. We went up the lead, and after another hundred yards or so it opened into a kind of lake with many islands of floating ice. The lake was a haven for murre. There were murre stringing overhead and murre perched on the ice and murre bobbing on the water. They were very tame, and I got a good look at them. They were pretty birds with vivid penguin plumage and long, sharp bills. Sitting erect on the ice, they even looked like penguins.

Pikonganna suddenly stiffened, and then sank slowly down on his plank. It was an alerting movement. Everybody tensed.

"*Ooguruk,*" he said, and pointed.

About a hundred and fifty yards to the right, a big, silvery bearded seal lay basking on a floating floe. It hadn't seen or heard us yet. Norbert cut the motors and we drifted silently toward the ice. Nobody spoke. The most accessible rifle of adequate calibre was a Remington .30/06, and the man closest to it was Fuller. It was Rychetnik's rifle, and he motioned to Fuller to take it. Nobody moved. Fuller swung the gun to his shoulder, steadied himself, and fired. A flight of murre veered loudly away. The seal gave a start, and lay still.

The boat nudged up to the floe, and Kunnuk vaulted over the gunwale and onto the ice. He had a revolver in his hand. Sam Mogg and Fuller jumped ashore and trotted after Kunnuk. Rychetnik and I got out on the ice and watched them. Kunnuk was the first to reach the seal. Apparently, it was still alive. He squatted down and shot it in the head. He put the revolver away and took out a hunting knife and cut two belt-loop slits in the skin just above the eyes. Sam Mogg and Fuller came sliding up, and Mogg threw Kunnuk a length of rope. Kunnuk threaded the rope through the belt-loop slits and made it fast, and then he and Mogg and Fuller dragged the seal across the floe to the boat. The seal was a young female. It was about six feet long and it weighed at least four hundred pounds, and Kunnuk and Fuller and Mogg were sweating when they got it up to the boat. They were grinning, too. Everybody was grinning, and Mogg slapped Fuller on the back. When Kunnuk and Fuller and Mogg had caught their breath, they rolled the seal over on its back, and Kunnuk got out his knife again and gutted and cleaned it. Then they hoisted the carcass over the gunwale and into the bow. The fur looked suddenly different. The brilliant silver lustre had begun to fade. By the time we were ready to leave, it was a dingy, leaden gray.

We moved along the lakelike lead. The wind and the tide were shifting the ice, and the lead grew wider and more open. There was open water now all the way to the looming cliffs. I stood up. There was open water everywhere ahead. An open lagoon stretched for two or three hundred yards between the shelf of anchored ice and the foot of the cliffs, and it seemed to encircle the island. We moved across the open water and into the shadow of the cliffs. Then, at a signal from Kunnuk, Norbert swung the boat to the left. We headed down the eastern face of the island. I looked up at the towering crags and pinnacles. Every ledge was a rookery. The rocks were alive with perching murre and kittiwakes and gulls and auklets and cormorants and puffins and terns.

Kunnuk turned around. He had his revolver in his hand. "You like to see some birds?" he said, and pointed the revolver overhead. "Just watch—I show you something."

He fired two shots, and then a third. The revolver was only a .22, but against the sounding board of water and rock it sounded like a bomb. It sounded like a hundred bombs. The shots went echoing up and down the face of the island, and a cloud of birds came screaming off the cliffs. They flew screaming over our heads and across the lagoon to the outer ice and then veered around and came streaming back. They came off the cliffs and over the water in waves—hundreds, thousands, tens of thousands of birds. It was impossible to even guess at the number.

The elderly woman leaned over my shoulder. "Ukivok is good place for eggs," she said. "All kinds of eggs." She smiled at me. "Very good to eat."

We sailed down the lagoon in a turbulence of birds. Many of them were birds that had never seen a man or a boat or heard a shot before, and it took them a long time to settle down again. The lagoon was irregularly shaped. Because of the broken line of the shifting outer ice, it was sometimes as wide as a lake and sometimes no more than a river. We followed it across a lake and through a little river and into another lake. I heard the motors cut off and felt the boat begin to drift. Pikonganna and Kunnuk were standing together on the lookout plank, and Sam Mogg and Rychetnik and Fuller were on their feet. Even Norbert was standing. I stood up, too. The lake we were in was the end of the lagoon.

Kunnuk came down off the plank. "O.K.," he said. "We go back. We go round the other way."

We all sat down. The motors started up, and the boat swung around, and we headed back up the lagoon. The boat suddenly slowed. Kunnuk was back on the lookout plank with Pikonganna, and Mogg was standing below them peering out between their legs. I couldn't tell what they were looking at. I didn't see anything unusual. We were approaching the upper end of the lake, and it looked much like the other end. And then I realized. The outer ice was moving in on some shift of wind or tide, and the little riverlike passage through which we had come had almost disappeared. The passage was about two hundred feet long, and ten or fifteen minutes ago it had been a good hundred feet wide. It now was hardly twenty.

The boat began to move again. Pikonganna and Kunnuk had come to some decision. We made our way across the last of the lake to the head of the passage. The passage had an ugly look. There was a ten-foot embankment of glassy ice on the island side, and the outer ice was pitted with holes and piled with pressure ridges, and it was moving fast. I could see it closing in. Rychetnik gave a kind of grunt.

"I don't like this very much," he said. "I don't think I like it at all. You know what this boat is made out of. If we get caught between the ice in there . . ."

"I don't like it, either," I said. "But I guess there isn't much choice."

"These cats know what they're doing," Fuller said. "I've never seen them take a chance they didn't have to."

The boat edged into the passage. The water was thick with chips and chunks of floating ice. We moved carefully between the embankment of anchored ice and the moving floe on one throttled-down motor. Norbert kept the boat inching along just off the lip of the floe, away from the height and bulk of the ice embankment, but every time I looked, the ice seemed higher and closer. I could already feel the cold of its breath. Kunnuk reached out with an ice lance and jabbed at the edge of the floe. He jabbed again, hard, and a slab of ice came loose and slid slowly into the water. The boy at the stern with Norbert poked it safely past the boat with an oar. It was rotten ice. The whole rim of the floe was rotten ice.

Kunnuk said something in Eskimo, and stepped up on the gunwale and jumped out on the floe. Mogg and Fuller followed him over, and Rychetnik and the boy at the stern followed them. They all had lances or boat hooks, and they spread out along the floe and began hacking at the rim of rotten ice. They worked just ahead of the inching boat, and Pikonganna hung over the bow with an oar and guided the slabs of floating ice to the island side of the passage. I found another oar and kept the ice moving and clear of the boat. Some of the slabs were the size of boulders, and it took all my strength and weight hanging on the oar to push them off and away. But I kept them moving, and the boat was also moving, and finally I raised my head and looked out over Pikonganna's shoulder and there was the end of the passage and a blue expanse of open water. Norbert shouted, and the women gave a quavering wail. We were through.

We went back up the eastern face of the island and around the northern end and down the western side. Everybody was talking and laughing. There was no ice anywhere on the western side except along the shore, but the island was the same. There were the same gray cliffs, the same patches of yellow lichen, the same thousands of screaming birds. There was no sign of a village, and no place where a village might even conceivably be built. So the village was down at the southern end of the island. We still had some distance to go. I looked at my watch, and I could hardly believe it. It had been nine hours since we stopped for lunch. It was almost nine o'clock.

Rychetnik had been dozing in the evening sun. He sat up and shook himself. "I'm getting kind of hungry," he said. "As a matter of fact, I'm starved."

"I've been thinking about our dinner," Fuller said. "I thought the first night on King Island we ought to have something real special. Anybody got any suggestions?"

"I suggest we all go down to the Four Seasons," Rychetnik said.

"We've got a ham," Fuller said. "It's one of those Polish hams. I guess we'll have that, and maybe some spaghetti."

"And a drink," I said.

"Don't worry about that," Rychetnik said.

The village was well around on the southern tip of the island. It was built on the slope of a chute of landslidden rocks. It hung on the slope about three hundred feet above a beach of ice and tumbled boulders, and it consisted of eighteen or twenty houses. The houses were wooden shacks with tarpaper roofs, and they were stepped out from the slope on tall wooden stilts. Scaffolding walks and ladderlike steps connected the houses, and a long flight of steps led down to the boulder beach.

"It looks even hairier closer up," Rychetnik said. "But I guess it's safe enough. The house we're going to stay in is the schoolhouse— what used to be the schoolhouse. The teacher left about ten years ago. It's the house with all those windows up there at the head of the steps. That's where I stayed when I was here before. It isn't any Hilton, but it's got four walls and a roof and some chairs to sit on and a table. It won't be too bad."

The boat turned in toward the shore, and I watched the village coming clearer. It was hard to think of it as an Eskimo village. It looked remoter than that. It looked Tibetan. A man came out on the balcony of one of the upper houses. There was a green and red and purple patchwork quilt hung over the railing to air. The man watched us for a moment. Then he raised both hands high over his head and waved. Pikonganna waved back. He was grinning from ear to ear. He reached down and slapped Kunnuk on the back.

"Home sweet home, boy," he said. "There's no place like home."

Kunnuk smiled and nodded. "That's right," he said.

# The Steeple

Not long ago, on an afternoon of wild winds and sudden silences, I drove out to the village of Sag Harbor to make a pilgrimage to the Whalers' Presbyterian Church there. Sag Harbor is on the north shore of the southeastern fluke of Long Island and covers a secluded point on Shelter Island Sound, near the head of Gardiners Bay. It was settled around the beginning of the eighteenth century. For a few years just before the Revolution, it was a busier port than New York; it once had as rich and restless a whaling fleet as New Bedford or Nantucket; it has been almost motionless since the Civil War; and it is full of big, splendid, creaky old houses and intimations of mortality. The Whalers' Church, although little more than a hundred years old, is its noblest and most disquieting structure. It would be arresting anywhere. Except for a mean and slovenly copy in Essex, Connecticut, it is the only building of its kind in the world.

The Whalers' Church was designed by Minard Lafever, a gifted and expensive New York architect, whose more accessible works include the Church of St. James, near Chatham Square, and the Church of the Holy Trinity, in Brooklyn, and it was put together by local shipbuilders and ships' carpenters. The foundation was laid in the spring of 1843 and the church was dedicated on May 16, 1844. It cost seventeen thousand dollars. That was an immense sum in the eighteen-forties (carpenters were paid a dollar and a half for a twelve-hour day, the finest St. Croix rum sold for three cents a glass, and clear Havana stogies were two cents each), but it was not considered excessive by Sag Harbor Presbyterians. Most of the parishioners who made substantial contributions to the building fund were whaling officers, shipyard owners, shipowners, or ship chandlers and outfitters, and several were among the wealthiest men on Long Island; practically all the members of the congregation, including farmers and shopkeepers, held rewarding shares in at least one whaler. The first Sag Harbor whaling voyage on record was made in 1775, by a brig called the Lucy; she returned home with some three hundred barrels of oil on that occasion. The last Sag Harbor whaler was the Myra; she put out in July, 1871, and never returned.

In the intervening years, Sag Harbor whalers made more than five hundred successful voyages, many of which lasted three or four years, and brought back between twenty-five and thirty million dollars' worth of whale oil, sperm oil, and whalebone. The first ship to sail through the Bering Strait was the Superior, a Sag Harbor whaler, in 1848. The first American ship to enter a Japanese port was the Manhattan, in 1845, commanded by Mercator Cooper, a Sag Harbor whaling captain; Commodore Matthew C. Perry, who is commonly celebrated for this feat, turned up off Japan eight years later. Between 1820 and 1850, Sag Harbor's richest period, the local fleet brought in a total of 83,102 barrels of sperm oil, 812,595 barrels of whale oil, and 6,728,809 pounds of bone, with an aggregate value of more than fifteen million dollars. The industry began to decline in the eighteen-fifties, and it collapsed in the sixties; an abundance of petroleum, which had just been discovered in western Pennsylvania, had all but put an end to the demand for whale oil. The Whalers' Church was completed in Sag Harbor's most vigorous year; the town's fleet in 1844 numbered sixty-three vessels, and its population was 3,621. Sag Harbor no longer has even the semblance of a fleet, its harbor is deserted except for a few pleasure craft in summer, its railroad station has been boarded up since 1939, and its population is 2,444.

Sag Harbor is surrounded on the north and east by the waters of Shelter Island Sound, and a sandy cove hems it in on the west. Above it, to the south, rises a wilderness of scrub oak and jack pine that stretches almost to the ocean, seven miles away. Three or four rambling, humpbacked roads, cut through the woods, link the village to the Montauk Highway, which skirts the seacoast. On the day of my visit I turned into one of these roads at about two o'clock. After a couple of miles, I passed a woman on a wobbly bicycle. Farther on, I passed a weathered sign: "Good Luck and Safe Return—Welcome to Sag Harbor." Just beyond it was a cemetery. Then the road curved, and I emerged abruptly into a wide, angular, downhill street of arching elms and peeling white clapboard houses. The houses sat close to the sidewalk, behind rickety picket fences; there were leaded fanlights over most of their doorways, and one had a widow's walk on the roof. An elderly man in a blue serge suit and an Army sweater was puttering around in one of the yards. He was the only human being in sight. I pulled up and asked him if he could direct me to the Whalers' Church. He leaned on the fence and gazed at me. "Want to have a look at it, eh?" he said. "Well, it's a sight. Should have come down here ten years ago, though, before the hurricane carried off the steeple. Wouldn't have been any need to ask your way then. You'd of seen it for yourself from here, downstreet, or anywhere. Far as that goes, you could see it from Montauk. That steeple was two hundred feet high, more or less, and there wasn't two parts of it alike. They were every one different. That steeple really tickled me. I enjoyed looking at it. Religion aside, of course. I run with the Methodists, when I go." The old man fished a package of chewing gum from his pocket, popped a stick into his mouth, and jerked his thumb in the direction I was headed. "Two blocks down, turn left at the blinker, and you'll see it," he said. "I guess there's enough of it left to hold you."

I thanked him and drove on down the windy, deserted street. The air smelled wet and salty. As I made the turn at the blinker, a ragged army of gulls wheeled overhead. Then I saw the church. It came hulking up through the heaving treetops—big and baleful and as white as an old clamshell. Set on a wooded knoll, well back from the street, between a row of splayed early-eighteenth-century cottages and a crumbling graveyard, it looked larger than Grand Central Station, and it held me. I parked my car and got out and stared at it. It is a numbing blend of the chaste, the finical, and the stolid. Its façade is predominantly Babylonian and Theban Egyptian in style.

The auditorium—of clapboard, slate-roofed, boxy, and severe—is pure meetinghouse Colonial. A kind of annex, jutting out in back, is mid-Victorian. From where I stood, at one end of a semicircular walk leading up to the church, only a corner of the main body of the building was visible. The auditorium is a hundred and thirty feet long, sixty-five feet wide, and the equivalent of three considerable stories in height, but the façade obscured it. A massive, shingle-sided, hundred-foot truncated pyramidal wooden tower, some forty feet square at the base and tapering to almost half that at the top, forms the center of the façade. It is flanked by two similar, though broader and slightly lower, wing pylons. Surmounting each of the pylons and the tower is a fragile parapet. The cornices are decorated with a complicated Corinthian frosting. A toothy row of antefixes conceals the eaves. Just below this is a banding of classic-Grecian verticals. An uncovered porch, with an iron-pipe railing, runs the width of the façade. Opening onto it are three narrow, story-high, white, panelled doors, one in the tower and one in each pylon. The antefixes are repeated on their cornices, and the center door is crowned by another parapet. Above each door, and rising almost to the roof line, is a tall window of opaque and faintly lavender small-paned glass. I stood there for a minute or two gazing up at the church, and then I started up the walk leading to the porch. It was hard to imagine a mighty steeple rearing above that vast, chalky face. The building didn't look at all incomplete. It didn't even look old. It looked like a brand-new mausoleum.

I tried all three doors and found them locked. As I turned uncertainly away from the last one, I heard voices approaching, and then a sudden shriek of laughter. I almost jumped. Then an unshaven old man in work clothes and a hunting cap came around the side of the building. With him was a somewhat younger woman. She had on a pink dress, a grass-green coat, and golden slippers, and there was a red patent-leather pocketbook under her arm. I went over to them. They were laughing and chattering, but they broke off when they saw me, and stopped dead. I said I had come out from New York to see the church and asked if the pastor was around.

"Here?" the man said, studying me closely. "Ain't he down to the Manse?"

His companion giggled. "If Reverend Crawford was here," she

said, "he'd have me down on my knees. He's been praying for me to find a job. I'm praying right along with him, too."

"He's down to the Manse," the man said. "Either that or he's out preaching a funeral."

"Probably a funeral," the woman said cheerfully. "There's nothing likelier in this town. How many did you say he had last week, Mr. Cleveland?"

"Four," Mr. Cleveland said. "I doubt there's one today, though."

The woman turned to me. "Mr. Cleveland, here, is sexton of the church," she said. "He knows everything that's going on. That's why I come by and see him—to learn the news."

"Sexton, janitor, superintendent, and a little bit of everything else," Mr. Cleveland said. "You might say I've got more jobs here than there is congregation. We had eighty turn up last Sunday. There's room in there for a thousand, spread out just four to the pew. I guess they used to fill her up—sides, center, and gallery—but not in my time. Nor in my dad's, neither. In the old days, most everybody in town was Presbyterian. The R.C.s got the edge now."

"I wonder why that is," the woman said. "Unless it's those Poles and Italians at the watch factory."

"Times change," Mr. Cleveland said. "I remember when there was steamboats running down to New York from here and over to New London, and Sag Harbor was the end of the main line of the Long Island Railroad. That was in the nineties before they built on out to Montauk and stuck us off on a branch. Now we ain't even on that. You must of drove out here—you don't look like you walked. Well, I've got the time and the right to open her up and let you in—done it before for visitors. But maybe you'd better get Crawford to take you through. Since you come all the way out from New York, he'd be sorry to miss you. You see that gray house with a fence around it down there at the end of the block—where that old dog is laying in the drive? That's the Manse. I'll show you one thing, though. You've heard about the famous steeple we had, I guess, and how it went down in the hurricane. September 21, 1938, at three-thirty in the afternoon, was the date. Well, see that patch of new-looking concrete in the walk there, alongside the burying-ground wall? That's where the butt of the steeple hit. I live just the other side of the burying ground, and I was looking out the window and I saw it go. I couldn't hardly believe my eyes. Why, that steeple had been there all my life. What happened was the wind caught under the louvers in the Sir Christopher Wren section. It lifted the whole shebang straight up in the air—the whole hundred and fifty-or-more feet of it—swung it clear of the building, and dropped it on the walk there. Then it toppled over into the burying ground and smashed to smithereens. All except the bell. That didn't get a scratch on it. We've got it set up inside now, in the lobby. I won't say I heard the bell ring, because I didn't. I was inside, and the wind was too loud. But I know people that did. It rang once, hanging up there in midair, just before it hit. And that patch there is the exact spot where the steeple come down."

"I've got a piece of it at home for a souvenir," the woman said. "I guess everybody in town has. Mine's part of the Chinese part."

I left Mr. Cleveland and his friend on the church steps and walked down to the Manse. The sidewalk tilted every which way, and there were tree roots as big as my arm pushing up through the cracks. Most of the houses in the block were so old that moss was growing on their roofs. The dog in the driveway made a half-hearted attempt to rise as I pushed through the front gate, and then slumped somnolently back. Before I could knock at the door, it swung open and a sleek, bald, broad-shouldered man of about forty looked out. He wore metal-rimmed glasses and had on a red flannel shirt, faded dungarees, and dirty white sneakers, and he was eating an apple. "Heard you at the gate," he said, a bit indistinctly. Then he swallowed, grinned, and added, "It's as good as a bell." I introduced myself and explained why I was there. "That's fine," he said. "I'm Donald Crawford. Excuse me." He tossed the core of his apple over my head, out into the street. "Come right in. You picked a good day for your visit. For me, anyway. This is my day off—hence these clothes. I've been burning some trash." I stepped into a dim hall. From upstairs came the sound of running water and an occasional wail. "That's my little helper," Mr. Crawford remarked. "Douglas, aged four. He's enduring a bath. Our other treasure is at school. Mary Alice is seven. Let's go in the parlor." I followed him into a small, high-ceilinged room gently ravaged by time and children. A tall, lanky, white-haired man in a sombre suit and a high collar was leaning against the mantel of a handsome white marble fireplace. In an ashtray at his elbow lay an elaborate spiral of apple peel. "This is Dr. Charles H. Tillinghast," Mr. Crawford said to me. "He hasn't got a care in the world. He's just retired after forty-nine years of dentistry, and he recently ended a long term as president of our church board of trustees. You're not interrupting anything. He just dropped by for a chat. How about it, Doctor? Would you like to go up to the church with us?"

Dr. Tillinghast extended me a bony hand. "My boy," he said, "it would be a privilege to show you through. Historic Sag Harbor and its proudest monument, the Whalers' Church, are the chief interests of my declining years. As you may know, we have here the second-largest number of authentic Colonial buildings of any community in the United States. We are exceeded only by Nantucket. But even Nantucket, if I may say so, has no such church as ours. My one regret is that our glorious steeple is gone. You've read of it, I'm sure. Perhaps you have seen pictures of it. A work of art." He shook his head. "It was the crowning glory of Minard Lafever's ecclesiastical masterpiece. I miss it as I would an old and cherished friend."

"I'll go get my coat," Mr. Crawford said.

Dr. Tillinghast nodded, cleared his throat, and continued, "It was a loss that everyone felt deeply. One of our local poetesses, the late Annie Cooper Boyd, wrote very movingly about it. I believe I have a copy of her poem here. You might care to glance at it." He drew a wallet from his pocket, extracted a tousled clipping, and handed it to me. The poem, eleven stanzas long, was entitled "The Steeple." It began:

> "The Steeple—what!—the Steeple—
> Don't say that IT has gone!"
> Thus spoke the village people
> With voice and face forlorn.

Another stanza read:

> Oh, lovely, lofty steeple,
> We loved thee from the heart—
> Thy curious construction,
> Thy myriad types of art!

"Of course," said Dr. Tillinghast as I returned the clipping, "we must be thankful that the church itself was spared."

Mr. Crawford, wearing an elegant covert-cloth topcoat, appeared in the hall doorway. I helped Dr. Tillinghast into his coat, he placed a floppy hat on his head, and we filed out to the street. Just outside the gate, Dr. Tillinghast halted. "Perhaps," he said, "we should call our young friend's attention to some of the historic points of interest adjacent to this particular corner. The magnificent Greek Revival edifice that you have undoubtedly noticed directly across the street is the old Benjamin Huntting place. Its architect was none other than Minard Lafever. I see that surprises you. I'll admit that the resemblance between Sag Harbor's two examples of the great Lafever's art is not pronounced. The answer lies in the fact that he was a man of great versatility. Captain Huntting was one of our whaling princes and, I'm proud to say, a prominent member of our church. In fact, like myself, he served as president of our board of trustees. His home was built in 1846. It was later purchased by Mrs. Russell Sage, whom we claim as a fellow-citizen and esteem as a generous civic benefactor."

"She put a new coat of paint on the church once," Mr. Crawford said.

"At least once," Dr. Tillinghast said. "Including the steeple. The old Huntting place is now our Whaling Museum. That large white clapboard structure over there on the right is the old Hannibal French mansion, built around 1800. And behind those trees in the distance is the old Customs House, built in 1790. In its yard is a boxwood bush that there is every reason to believe was grown from a slip presented to our first Collector of Port by Martha Washington herself. Our port, unfortunately, was discontinued in 1905, but the old Customs House, quite properly, has been preserved."

"Don't forget the Manse, Doctor," Mr. Crawford said. He grinned at me and began to move on up the street. "Built in eighteen-twenty-something and never restored. It's a good thing I'm handy."

"I know, Donald," Dr. Tillinghast said mildly. "As I recall, Mr. Barrett often said the same."

"My predecessor," Mr. Crawford explained. "I'm Number Nineteen in the line. The ministry here goes back to 1794. It gives me a funny feeling sometimes to realize that this church had already gone through four generations of ministers before my home town was even founded."

"You're not from around here?" I asked.

"Hardly," Mr. Crawford said. "I'm from Chicago—Winnetka, to be exact. If you'll forgive me, Doctor, I'm not sure that I'd ever even heard of Sag Harbor until I received my call. That was only back in 1940. I must say it seems like a lifetime ago, though. Time sags along pretty slowly in Sag Harbor."

Dr. Tillinghast smiled a thin smile. "The name of Sag Harbor, as Donald knows, does not refer to that, however," he said. "It derives from a Shinnecock Indian word, *sagaponack*, which means 'place of the groundnuts.' Groundnuts are an edible root, something like a potato."

"Actually," Mr. Crawford said, "my call to Sag Harbor wasn't much more unexpected than my call to the ministry. My mother has never really got over that. Selling stocks and bonds was more the custom in our family. I may not look it, but I used to be a bond salesman. As soon as I got out of Yale—I was class of '28—I went right into a brokerage house back home. Sold bonds all day and danced all night. Then the market crashed. That did something to me. It wasn't simply a matter of economics. I can't explain it— I walked around in a daze. Then, one Sunday night in November, 1929, I wandered into the old Moody Church, on North LaSalle Street. That evening changed my entire life. I came out converted. I went on selling bonds, of course. I had to. But I spent my nights at the Moody Bible Institute, studying the Bible and making up for lost time. When I was ready—in 1936—I quit my job and came East and started all over again, at Princeton Theological Seminary. My family—well, one of my aunts—helped put me through. I was ordained in 1940. That was an eventful year for me. I was ordained, I got married, and I got this call. My wife is a Philadelphian. We were on our honeymoon when the call came and she cried for hours." He shrugged. "She likes it here now—we both do. Sag Harbor's a little off the beaten trail, but there's a tremendous spiritual challenge here. When a whole town lives in the past . . . I mean there are some extraordinary problems."

"Youth is always restless," Dr. Tillinghast said comfortably. He turned to me. "It might interest you to know that the Long Island

*Herald,* founded in Sag Harbor in 1791, was the first newspaper published on Long Island. No one would have called this off the beaten path a hundred years ago. One of America's greatest preachers, Edward Hopper, served our church from 1852 to 1863, and it was the daring seamen of Sag Harbor who inspired him to write his immortal hymn 'Jesus, Savior, Pilot Me.' James Fenimore Cooper lived here for some years, before he established himself as a writer. 'The Pioneers' and 'The Sea Lions' are both full of Sag Harbor. Why, this very street has known the tread of half the races of mankind. It was nothing in the old days to see Fiji Islanders, Malayans, Kanakas, Chinamen, Portuguese, Shinnecocks, and Montauks, and heaven only knows what else, roaming all over town. I imagine you've read 'Moby Dick.' Old Melville knew what he was doing when he had his pagan harpooner Queequeg brought to America on a Sag Harbor whaler."

"Well," Mr. Crawford said, with a wave of his hand, "there she blows—the church that whale oil built. I sometimes think that God placed me in Sag Harbor to humble me, but He certainly gave me a beautiful church."

The sight of the church was momentarily silencing. Familiarity didn't seem to diminish it. Even Dr. Tillinghast gazed at it without comment. There was no sign of Mr. Cleveland or his friend. Nobody spoke until we were halfway up the walk. Then Dr. Tillinghast gave a short, puzzled laugh. "In all fairness," he said, "I should point out that our church has attracted a few—a very few—unfavorable criticisms. We had an architect visiting here one summer who called it a hodgepodge. The unconventionality of its parts apparently blinded him to the beauty of the whole. He was from one of the newer settlements in the Middle West."

I remarked that Lafever must have been an extremely imaginative man.

"Lafever scorned the commonplace," Dr. Tillinghast said. "The old Benjamin Huntting place, though traditional, has many unusual touches. But I'm not sure that the style of our church was entirely Lafever's idea. His was the guiding hand, of course, but it must be remembered that he was dealing here with men who sailed the Seven Seas and had absorbed the flavor of foreign lands. They had their own ideas. What Lafever did was combine their impressions with his own. I think he was also inspired to suggest something of their courageous way of life. Look at the curious design of the railings up there on the tower and the pylons and over the center door. One of our less appreciative visitors said they looked like a row of lollipops." A trace of pain crossed Dr. Tillinghast's face. "Of course," he went on, "that motif is a stylized version, in what I take to be the Gothic manner, of the whaler's blubber spade. That would be obvious to anyone who had examined the fine collection of old Sag Harbor whaling implements at the Museum. Ridicule comes easy to some people. It may surprise you to hear that even our steeple was not completely immune to criticism. The Sag Harbor *Corrector*, now defunct, once called it 'fantastic' and Lafever 'bewildered.' If you could only have seen that glorious steeple! Perhaps I can describe it to you. It rose, naturally, from the top of the tower, and the height of it was truly majestic—one hundred and eighty-seven feet. Its height was another seafaring note. Our mariners wanted their church spire to serve as a landmark, visible to the returning ship as it rounded Montauk Point. For many years, a whale-oil beacon lamp at the pinnacle was lighted every night."

"I've read somewhere that it used to be noted on the U.S. Coast and Geodetic Survey maps," Mr. Crawford said.

"Very likely," Dr. Tillinghast said. "Our steeple was composed in three tapering sections, each smaller in diameter than the one beneath it. I don't think it was accidental that it resembled somewhat the sea captain's spyglass in use at that time. I doubt, too, if anyone but a shipwright could have raised it. It was raised by ox power, each section pulled up through the inside of the preceding one. The lowest section, in which the bell was installed, was in the seventeenth-century English style of Sir Christopher Wren, and extremely decorative. The main feature of it was an octagonal colonnade. In its pediment were four beautiful clocks. The derivation of the second section is uncertain. It was probably either Greek or, as some experts have suggested, Phoenician. Its chief ornamentation, at any rate, was a series of long panels, in which were cut the ancient Phoenician swastika. That was a symbol, I understand, of good luck. The topmost section was a replica of a Chinese pagoda. Needless to say, the entire structure was made of the finest Suffolk County white pine, chosen and seasoned by our own shipbuilders, and every inch of it was hand-carved." Dr. Tillinghast shook his head. "No," he said, "I hardly think that you or any person with a feeling for beauty would have called our steeple 'fantastic.'"

"Is there any prospect of restoring it?" I asked.

"We talk about it," Mr. Crawford said. "A year or two ago, we even had an architect out from New York to look into it. He said it could be done. There are plenty of good photographs of the old steeple around that an expert could go by. There hasn't been so much talk of it since we got his estimate, though. It was a little over seventy-five thousand dollars." Mr. Crawford unlocked the center door, pushed it open, and waved us in. "That's just about five times the original cost of the whole church."

We entered the lobby, big and square and gloomy. Opening off it were three panelled oak doors leading to the auditorium and the flanking pylons. The walls were dark and hung with marble memorial plaques, one of which read:

REV. SAMUEL KING,
*A NATIVE OF ENGLAND,*
who departed this life Nov. 29th 1833;
after having ministered to this
congregation
one year and three months,
in the 42 year of his life.

THIS TABLET
*as a token of respect*
*is devoted to the memory of a stranger and*
*a good man.*
*"The memory of the just is blessed."*

Mounted on a low wooden frame in the middle of the lobby was a mighty bell. Dr. Tillinghast caught up a knotted end of rope attached to it as we passed. "Listen to this tone," he said, and struck the bell a savage whack. It gave an exhausted moan. "Sound as a dollar," he said. "I venture to say not many bells could survive such a fall."

"God spared what He deemed essential," Mr. Crawford said. "If you like, I'll take you up on the bell deck—what used to be the bell deck—before we leave. But right now . . ." He opened the auditorium door and took me by the arm. The three of us stepped into a silent immensity of whiteness. At the foot of a long center aisle, carpeted in faded green and lined with boxed pews, was a high rostrum. It was set in a *trompe-l'oeil* circular arcade, flanked on either side by a door, and framed by a pair of round, fluted Corinthian columns and two square pilasters that rose, well over fifty feet, to a coffered ceiling. Two steeply inclined overhanging galleries, faced with an intricate frieze of carved volutes and rosettes, ran the length of the side walls. Behind each of them was a row of tall, tinted windows, ablaze with frosty lavender light. Except for the carpet, three tortuous black chairs on the rostrum, and a narrow trimming of rich, red mahogany along the sides and backs of the pews, the entire chamber was salt-white, and they made it look even whiter. For an instant, it was as dazzling as sun on snow.

Mr. Crawford dropped his hand from my arm. "It's beautiful, isn't it?" he said. "I don't mean to seem proud." I said, quite truthfully, that I'd never seen a more handsome room. "No," he said. "Of course, it's a few sizes too big for us now. I guess it always was. The sad thing is that it was built for the future. A hundred years ago, you know, there was a tremendous religious revival sweeping the country, and at the same time Sag Harbor was getting more prosperous every year. We had the main floor pretty well filled for our centennial celebration. Maybe someday . . ." He sighed and smiled. "Those doors on either side of the platform go into the Sunday school. That's a good, big room too."

"The Sunday-school annex is a later addition," Dr. Tillinghast said, without interest. Moving briskly down the aisle, he continued, "Let me call your attention to the fine Cuban-mahogany trimming on these pews—a very unusual touch. One of our whaling captains selected the wood himself in Cuba and brought it home in his own ship. The workmanship is that of shipwrights. You may have seen some photographs of old ships' railings that resembled it. And notice the little silver nameplates and numerals on the pew doors. That's another pretty touch. Up to about the Civil War, I understand, every pew was also furnished with a fine brass spittoon. Those old Sag Harbor whalers were a rough lot." He shook his head with a kind of admiration and pointed up at the wall. "I mentioned the Phoenician-swastika motif," he went on. "Well, there it is again, in that frieze just under the ceiling. Also, the columns supporting the galleries are exactly like those that formed the colonnade in the Sir Christopher Wren section of the steeple. You see how perfectly Lafever tied everything together?"

"There's another example of it, up there in the choir loft," Mr. Crawford said, turning back toward the lobby. He nodded in the direction of a third, and smaller, gallery, which linked the two side ones just above the door to the lobby. In a niche in the wall behind it stood what appeared to be a replica in miniature of the church's towering façade. I could even make out a row of tiny blubber spades around the parapets. "Our organ," he said. "You can see the pipes through those vents in the casing." He glanced at his watch. "If we're going up on the bell deck, we'd better get started. It's a good climb. How about you, Doctor?"

"You flatter me, Donald," Dr. Tillinghast said. "I'll try to content myself here below. I think, in fact, I'll sit down."

We left Dr. Tillinghast, looking wistfully after us, among the melancholy plaques in the vestibule. A circular staircase in the pylon to the right led us up to a bare anteroom on the gallery level. We went through a door into the choir loft, where there was another door, about the size of a transom, leading into the base of the tower. Mr. Crawford squirmed through this one. "I don't know who designed this," he said, "but he must have been thinking of a porthole." I followed him into a cobwebby cubicle behind the organ niche. It was not quite pitch-dark. "Watch yourself, now," he said. "These steps are steep." We went up two angular flights to a twilit landing, where Mr. Crawford directed my hand to the rail of an almost perpendicular stepladder. Then he disappeared overhead, breathing hard. I felt my way slowly after him to another landing and another ladder. We were well up in the tower now, and I could hear the sound of the wind outside. Light appeared above, and broadened into a tinted window, extending a foot or two above the level of a third landing, where we found ourselves in a forest of bare joists, beams, and uprights. On one of the uprights was painstakingly carved "J.M.F., Sept. 27, 1862." Mr. Crawford leaned limply against a foot-square, hand-hewn pillar. It was anchored, like a mast, in a thick, cast-iron shoe bolted to a wooden girder. "This was one of the steeple supports," he said, giving it an indifferent pat. "The only one that held. It snapped off higher up. The others sailed away with the steeple. Listen to that wind up there. They tell me the steeple used to shake like a tree on a day like this. One more climb and we'll be in the middle of that gale." He moved off along a catwalk of teetering planks. It ended at the foot of a runged ladder, which rose some twenty feet to a trapdoor in the ceiling. The ladder was as unsteady as a rope as I followed him up. "Hold your hat," he said, and heaved back the trap. We stepped out, coattails flying and trousers flapping, onto a creaking tin roof. It seemed like the top of the world.

We gazed down, over roofs and treetops and the spires of three humbler churches, at the deserted harbor. Beyond it lay the gray-green plain of the sea and the hazy gray sand bluffs of faraway points and islands. "That's Shelter Island, straight ahead," Mr. Crawford said, hunching deeper into his coat. "Over there to the left of it is Noyack Bay. The smudge in the distance is the north fluke of Long Island—we're about on a line here with Greenport. That's another old whaling ruin. Off to the right, there, you can see the Rhode Island shore on a good, bright day."

I said it was quite a view. "It must have been magnificent from the top of the old steeple," I added.

"I suppose so," Mr. Crawford said. He turned and looked at me. "I suppose," he went on, "you noticed that our organ casing hasn't got a steeple. It was made that way. Prophetic, wasn't it?" There was an odd expression on his face. "I'll tell you what I think," he said. "Our steeple wasn't blown down by accident. These people here had got so they were worshipping the steeple more than they did God. So He took it away."

# A Window on the Oligocene

There are few more beautiful natural parks than the mountain valley that encloses the village of Florissant (pop. 102), in Teller County, Colorado, about a hundred miles southwest of Denver, on the western slope of the Front Range of the Rockies. This valley has been variously known as South Park and Castello's Ranch, but it now takes its name from the village. It is ten miles long and a mile or two wide, and it follows a gently winding course, with many sudden, serpentine arms. The valley floor is a rolling meadow. It flows, deep in grass, around an occasional thrust of rust-red granite outcrop, and it is framed on the east and west by low hills crowned with open groves of ponderosa pine. Florissant is high country—almost nine thousand feet—but above its highest hills, encircling the infinite distance, are the peaks of higher mountains. There are antelope in the Florissant valley, and deer and elk and bear and badgers and coyotes and porcupines, and in July the meadows are a garden of wild flowers—bluebells, yellow clover, purple locoweed, pink trumpet phlox, alpine daisies, brown-eyed Susans, flaming Indian paintbrush. The beauty of Florissant, however, is not its only natural glory. It has another, a rarer and a richer one. Beneath the flowering Florissant meadows lies a treasury of paleontological history. Florissant is one of the richest repositories of plant and insect fossils in the world.

A fossil is an impression of a prehistoric organism which has been preserved in the crust of the earth. Fossils are formed in many ways. These include freezing, drying, petrifaction (or the replacement of organic by mineral matter), and encasement under pressure in asphalt, amber, sandstone, shale, or volcanic ash. The Florissant fossil beds were formed by a series of volcanic eruptions that began some thirty-eight million years ago. This places the beds, by geologic time, in the Oligocene epoch of the Cenozoic era. Florissant was then, as now, a valley, but it was a highland rather than a mountain valley, and it had a mild, humid, probably subtropical climate. A wandering stream flowed south through the valley, and the banks of the stream and the slopes above it were covered with willow and oak and pine and beech and giant sequoia. The first, progenitive volcanic eruption changed that distant scene. Its convulsions deposited a levee of volcanic mud at the mouth of the valley, blocking the outward flow of the stream, and the stream thus dammed became a pond, and the pond became a lake. Fish flourished there, and insects swarmed, and trees and shrubs grew dense along the shore. The volcano presently came to life again, and for perhaps three million years there were frequent wild eruptions. With every eruption, a cloud of fine volcanic ash blew into Florissant. The ash fell thickly on the lake, and as it settled it carried with it to the bottom a multitude of leaves and insects and tiny fish and stored them there in a thin, impressionable casing. Millennia passed, and the layered deposits of silt and ashy shale accumulated. The lake slowly shrank from a depth of forty feet to only a foot or two, and finally drained dry. It was then, around thirty-four million years ago, that a final and cataclysmic eruption occurred, and the whole of the lake was buried in a flood of boiling lava. That perfectly sealed the formed and forming fossils, and preserved them for man's eventual discovery.

The Florissant fossil beds were discovered almost a hundred years ago. A field geologist named A. C. Peale is generally accepted as their discoverer. Peale made his find in the course of a study for the United States Geological and Geographical Survey in the summer of 1873. A few years earlier, in 1870, the community that came to be called Florissant (from *floraison*, meaning "season of flowers") had been established as a trading post by a wanderer known to local history as Judge James Castello, but if Castello had then seen and recognized the fossil beds that lay in his domain, he left no record of the fact. Peale did. He included an account of his find in his formal survey report. "About five miles from the mouth [of Beaver Creek]," he noted, "around the settlement of Florissant, is an irregular basin filled with modern lake deposits. The entire basin is not more than five miles in diameter. The deposits extend up the branches of the creek, which all unite near Florissant. Between the branches are granite islands appearing above the beds, which themselves rest on granite. Just below Florissant, on the north side of the road, are bluffs not over 50 feet in height, in which are good exposures of the various beds. The following section gives them from the top downward: 1. Coarse conglomeritic sandstone. 2. Fine-grained, soft, yellowish-white sandstone, with bands that are more or less argillaceous, and containing fragments and stems of leaves. 3. Coarse gray and yellow sandstone. 4. Chocolate-colored clay shales with fossil leaves. At the upper part, these shales are black, and below pass into— 5. Whitish clay shales. These last form the base of the hill. The beds are all horizontal. Scattered around are fragments of a trachyte [a volcanic rock], which probably caps the beds. . . . I had thought it possible that the beds were of Pliocene age. The specimens obtained from bed [i.e., stratum] No. 4, of the section above, were submitted to Professor Lesquereux, who informs me that they are . . . 'Upper Miocene.' . . . The shales were so soft and friable that it was rather difficult to obtain any specimens. About one mile south of Florissant, at the base of a small hill of sandstone, capped with conglomerate, are 20 or 30 stumps of silicified wood."

The authoritative Professor Lesquereux to whom Peale submitted his specimens for dating was the celebrated Swiss-born American paleobotanist Leo Lesquereux, and it was he, together with two equally eminent associates, who made the first scientific evaluations of the Florissant fossiliferous shales. His associates were the paleozoologist Edward Drinker Cope and the founder of American insect paleontology Samuel Hubbard Scudder. Scudder was the first scientist to follow Peale to Florissant. He made the first of many visits there in the summer of 1877, and spent five strenuous days examining the visible beds and collecting fossils for later laboratory study. His account of that first visit, which appeared as part of a comprehensive report ("The Tertiary Lake Basin at Florissant, Colo., between South and Hayden Parks") in the *Bulletin of the United States Geological and Geographical Survey* in 1882, was ecstatic. "The very shales of the lake itself," he noted, "in which the myriad plants and insects are entombed, are wholly composed of volcanic sand and ash; fifteen meters or more thick they lie, in alternating layers of coarser and finer material. . . . The upper half has been eroded and carried away, leaving, however, the fragmentary remains of this great ash deposit clinging to the borders of the basin and surrounding the islands; a more convenient arrangement for the present explorer could not have been devised. . . . The insects preserved in the Florissant basin are wonderfully numerous, this single locality having yielded in a single summer more than double the number of specimens which the famous localities at Oeningen, in Bavaria, furnished Heer in thirty years. Having visited both places I can testify to the greater prolificness of the Florissant beds . . . and the quarries are fifty times as extensive and far more easily worked."

Scudder also inspected the "silicified wood" to which Peale had alluded. "Our examination of the deposits of this lacustrine basin," he noted, "was principally made in a small hill, from which perhaps the largest number of fossils have been taken, lying just south of the house of Mr. Adam Hill, and upon his ranch. Like the other ancient islets of this upland lake, it now forms a mesa or flat-topped hill about ten or a dozen meters high. . . . Around its eastern base are the famous petrified trees, huge, upright trunks, standing as they grew, which are reported to have been five or six meters high at the advent of the present residents of the region. Piecemeal they have been destroyed by vandal tourists, until now not one of them rises more than a meter above the surface of the ground, and many of them are entirely leveled; but their huge size is attested by the relics, the largest of which can be seen to have been three or four meters in diameter. These gigantic trees appear to be sequoias." Scudder ended his report with a new estimate, concurred in by both Lesquereux and Cope, of the age of the Florissant beds. They were neither Pliocene (two to ten million years ago) nor Miocene (ten to twenty-seven million years ago) in origin. They were Oligocene.

The first Florissant fossils to be properly studied were those collected by Scudder in 1877. That visit, though brief, was prophetically productive. In the mere five days that Scudder spent in the beds, he and three companions (two fellow-scientists and the local rancher Hill) gathered a total of around five thousand specimens. The quality of the material also was prophetically high. "The shales of Florissant," Lesquereux enthusiastically noted, "have preserved the most delicate organisms—feathers, insects, small flies, petals, even anthers and stamens of flowers." Lesquereux, being a botanist, reviewed the plant specimens. He was able to distinguish some ninety different species. All of them were species long extinct, but most were recognizable as prototypes of modern plants. Fossil vertebrates were reviewed by Cope. He found few satisfactory specimens, and fewer species. His report listed eight species of fish and two of birds—one a kind of plover and the other a finch. Scudder himself reviewed the insect and arachnid fossils, and it was chiefly his report that brought the Florissant beds to international scientific attention. He tentatively identified literally hundreds of species. They included thirty species of wasps, fifty species of ants, eight species of flies, fourteen species of spiders, five species of grasshoppers, sixty-five species of the order that embraces aphids, cicadas, and leafhoppers, and—to his particular delight—a wealth of butterflies. "Having examined more than ten years ago all the butterflies that were known in the European Tertiaries," he wrote in a separate survey report, "the American forms that have been exhumed at Florissant, in Colorado, in presumably Oligocene beds, have especially interested me. There are, altogether, seven species, more than have been found at any other locality in the world, and only two less than all that are known in the imago state from European deposits."

The paleontological importance of Florissant that Scudder first proclaimed has been ardently confirmed by many other paleontologists. At least a dozen major scientific expeditions have worked the Florissant beds and assembled large and comprehensive collections. Scudder added to his original collection by almost annual visits until his retirement in 1892. The first academic expedition to Florissant was sponsored by Princeton University. Its members worked there through the summer of 1880. That study was followed, in 1902, by a second Princeton expedition, this one jointly led by Henry Fairfield

Osborn, of the American Museum of Natural History, and W. B.
Scott, of the British Museum. Other expeditions have come to Florissant from the American Museum itself, the Denver Museum of Natural History, the University of Colorado, the University of Iowa, Washington State University, Humboldt (California) State College (led
by the distinguished paleontologist H. D. MacGinitie), and the University of California, and Florissant fossils are prominent in the collections of most notable natural-history museums. There has always been
plenty for all. The Florissant deposits are extraordinarily rich. According to a recent computation by Frank M. Carpenter, Fisher Professor
of Natural History at Harvard, they have yielded up some eighty
thousand explicit specimens of insects alone, and fossil plants are
even more abundant. This multitude of specimens represents well
over a thousand different species of life—around eleven hundred insects and arachnids, a hundred and forty-four plants, and sixteen
vertebrates. The insect specimens include a total of nine species of
butterflies and four species of tsetse flies, the now uniquely African
vector of trypanosomiasis, or sleeping sickness. Moreover, despite a
century of scientific scrutiny, the variety of the Florissant beds has
almost certainly not yet been exhausted. Every expedition turns up
new material. As recently as 1965, on a casual, one-day visit, a United
States Geological Survey paleontologist named Estella B. Leopold
discovered a fossil palm leaf, the first such specimen ever unearthed
at Florissant, and a totally unexpected find. It was also—like most
of the Florissant fossils—an excellent specimen.

The diverse and overflowing excellence of the Florissant fossil beds
is not their only distinction. They are equally distinguished in the
eyes of science by their age. Most other beds laid down in the expanses
of the Tertiary period of the Cenozoic era (from two to seventy
million years ago) are either younger or older than those at Florissant.
Florissant stands midway in time between the Miocene epoch, which
began twenty-seven million years ago, and the Eocene epoch, which
began fifty-five million years ago, and its fossiliferous shales are thus
a clear and precious view of life through several million otherwise
inscrutable years. There is only one other Rocky Mountain source
of Oligocene fossil plants. That is a bed at Ruby Valley, in Montana,
but specimens there are so few and far between that collectors work
it not by hand with a geologic hammer but with a bulldozer. The

Florissant record has scope as well as clarity. Its documentation of a particular place at a particular time is almost incomparably complete. The freak of nature that created Florissant preserved in each of its several stratifications a comprehensive flora and fauna—a total ecosystem. "If a single layer of paper shale in the Florissant beds could be uncovered simultaneously over its entire surface," Dr. Leopold has said, "we would have a detailed picture—a photograph in rock— of Florissant as it was some thirty-eight million years ago. As a volcanic tomb, Florissant is a kind of Pompeii of the Oligocene. It's a kind of Dead Sea Scroll of evolution. There is simply nothing like it."

Florissant was for centuries an occasional Indian hunting ground. The Utes camped and hunted there on their summer raids against the Pueblo towns in what are now New Mexico and Arizona, and so, at times, did the nomadic Arapahos. The white discoverers of Florissant were the mountain men of the second generation. They trapped and explored and roughly mapped that part of the Rockies in the eighteen-forties and fifties. A tall tale of the period, told by a trapper on his return to Taos from a mountain journey (and recorded in a government guide to the area), was probably inspired by the petrified stumps at Florissant: "Pa'dners, I seed a pewtrified forest of pewtrified trees with their pewtrified limbs chockful of pewtrified birds a-singing of pewtrified songs." With the arrival, in the eighteen-seventies, of the trader James Castello and the rancher Adam Hill and others of their kind, the settlement of Florissant began, and the valley is now—hills and meadows and fossil beds—in well-documented private ownership. The owners of the Florissant valley are cattlemen; the growing season there is too short for any crop but grass. One of the dozen present owners of its twelve thousand acres operates a small tourist concession on the side. Two of them own lands embracing the remains of the petrified stumps. One of these also owns the bed from which Scudder extracted his first collection of fossils. This bed is open, for a fee, to the public, and visiting scientists have always been freely and warmly welcome there. They have also always been hospitably received by the owners of the other celebrated fossil beds—the bed worked by the first Princeton expedition, the University of California bed, a bed exposed by a cutting dug in 1887 for the now abandoned Colorado & Midland Railroad. The respect of the owners of Florissant for science has undoubtedly been a factor in the preservation of its fossil beds for continued scientific study. It has not, however, been an important one. Florissant has been largely preserved by the accident of nature that made it cattle country.

It has long been felt that the fossil riches of Florissant are too fragile to be so lightly guarded. The desirability of some defense against the human compulsion to rearrange nature which would be stronger than a long winter and a short summer was briefly considered as early as 1921. In that year, a group of interested scientists and others suggested that Florissant be brought into the protective embrace of the National Park Service. The suggestion received a politely sympathetic hearing, but no action was taken, and the interest of even its sponsors faded away and finally vanished under the impact of the Depression and the Second World War. It was revived, in 1953, by Edmund B. Rogers, then (he has since retired) the superintendent of Yellowstone National Park, with a testimonial based on first-hand exploration and entitled "Florissant Fossil Shale Beds, Colorado." Rogers' recommendation excited sufficient influential interest to set in motion the standard salvational procedure. This involved a pilot study, a preliminary report, and a formal proposal, and it proceeded at the standard pace. A formal proposal to preserve six thousand of the twelve thousand acres at Florissant as a Florissant Fossil Beds National Monument was approved by the director of the National Park Service in 1962. The following year, an enabling bill was introduced in the House of Representatives. It died, ignored. A similar bill was introduced in 1965, and it was similarly received. Two years later, in 1967, the House was offered a third Florissant bill. An amendment to it reduced the size of the proposed Monument from six thousand to one thousand acres. This truncated preserve attracted a wave of penny-pinching support, and the bill was approved with little opposition and sent along to the Senate. There it once more died. Another year went by and another Florissant bill was conceived. The new proposal differed from its predecessor in that it restored the cut in acreage and originated in the Senate. It was introduced on February 4, 1969. A few days later, an identical bill was introduced in the House. The winter passed, and also the spring. Then, on June 20th, the Senate approved its Florissant bill. The House bill remained in committee. Summer came on.

I went out to Colorado toward the end of July and paid a visit to Florissant. I saw it in the company of one of its many champions, Theodore R. Thompson, then the superintendent of Rocky Mountain National Park, at Estes Park, Colorado. He picked me up in Denver in a green Park Service station wagon at around eight o'clock on a hot, dry, cloudless morning. We drove south on the throughway to Colorado Springs, and then west through Manitou Springs and under the loom of Pikes Peak and over the crest of the Front Range at Divide and down the long western slope between browning grasslands and scattered groves and climbing woods of aspen and ponderosa pine. We passed a lonely filling station with a sign over the door: "We're from Illinois. Where are you from?" There were mountains, some of them still furrowed with snow, all around the horizon. A highway sign appeared ahead: "Florissant 8 Mi." Beyond it was a piercing orange Day-Glo billboard: "Westwood Lake Estates." The highway began to climb. Another billboard came into view: "Trout Haven Estates 2½ Mi." A gravel road led off to the left. Another mile, and another billboard appeared: "Colorado Mountain Estates. ½ Acre Lots." Then another: "Wagon Tongue Home Sites— Florissant."

"This country is changing fast," Thompson said. "That's why we're fighting hard for the Monument. We think it's now or never. It used to be just tourists here. They'd stop and then drive on. Now it's subdivisions—vacation houses. Everybody wants an A-frame in the mountains."

"Why an A-frame?" I said.

Thompson shrugged. "They're practical," he said. "Especially in snow country. And they're easy to maintain. But I think it's more than that. The A-frame is a kind of status symbol out here now."

We went down and around a bend. There was a rutted road on the left and a big welcoming billboard: "Lots. $15 Down. $15 Month." The roadbed climbed steeply up to a cluster of new houses. One of them was an A-frame.

"This is the edge of the Monument," Thompson said. "The proposed area all lies south of the highway and beyond that ridge over there. That's the village straight ahead. That's Florissant."

Florissant was a highway hamlet. Most of it was strung out along the right-hand side of the highway—a liquor store, a shingle-sided post office, a filling station, a real-estate office. On the other side were a log-cabin motel and café. A man in overalls was sitting on a bench in front of the post office. There was a billboard sign near the real-estate office: "4 Seasons Fun. Wilderness Estates." We turned left at the motel onto a gravel road that led south through a break in the ridge. The road wound up through open groves of pine and rolling wild-flower meadows. Black Angus cattle were grazing knee-deep in flowers in the meadows. A sky-blue bluebird—a mountain bluebird—flew across the road and into a clump of trees. This was the Florissant valley. This was the Florissant I had heard and read about. On a rise a mile or so away stood a long, low clapboard building with a covered gallery all around it.

"That's the Singer place," Thompson said. "It used to be the Florissant railroad depot, back in the old Colorado & Midland days. Bob Singer bought it and had it moved up there in 1924. The Singers have a little over eight hundred acres in the area, and their land includes some petrified stumps and a very good fossil bed. As a matter of fact, it's old Scudder's bed, and you'll want to see it. Their main business is cattle, but they also run a museum and tourist operation in the summer. If the Monument ever goes through, their house will probably be the administration building. Temporarily, anyway."

"How do the Singers feel about the Monument?" I said.

"Oh, they're for it," he said. "They see the need. They want to protect the beds. Most of the longtime owners here want the Monument. Except that some of them are getting a little impatient. You saw that development back there on the highway. That could have been part of the Monument. So could some of the lakebed west of Florissant. It was included in all the Monument plans until the owner finally got tired of waiting for Congress to act, and sold it. Now it's what they call Colorado Mountain Estates. And there's another, even bigger piece of the Monument that has just been sold to land-development companies."

We parked in a parking lot at one end of the Singer house. I got out to stretch my legs while Thompson went off to look for Bob Singer. The Singer house was unmistakably a vintage railroad station. It had a bow-window bulge in front that must have been the stationmaster's office, and the encircling covered gallery was the remains of the old passenger platform. I looked off across the valley. It was easy to visualize the railroad station as it had once been. I could easily picture the group of turn-of-the-century paleontologists climbing down from the red plush Pullman cars. I could see their heavy, high-buttoned suits and their high-crowned derby hats and their stern mustached faces. They were as sharp and true as a period photograph. But I couldn't picture anything of the past that lay under the meadows. All I could see were the rolling meadows flowering in the sun, and they looked like any pretty mountain meadows.

Thompson came back around the corner of the house. With him was a tall, tanned boy of seventeen or eighteen. He was a serious-looking boy. Thompson introduced us.

"This is Tim Singer," he said. He reached into the car and brought out a roll of plastic specimen bags and two geologic hammers. He handed me one of the hammers and stuck the bags in his pocket. "Tim grew up in this country, and he knows his fossils. He's going to show us around the old Scudder bed."

"I could show you something else, too," Tim said. "I'll show you our biggest petrified sequoia, if you want to see it. It's more or less on the way."

"I'd like to see it," I said.

"It's a fine specimen," Thompson said.

We followed a path up a slope behind the house. Halfway up the slope, the path levelled out and broadened into a sunken shelf. A big, furrowed, marble-like column was rooted in the middle of the shelf, like a fountain in a formal garden. That was the sequoia. Tim cleared his throat and changed his voice.

"This is the biggest petrified tree in the world," he said. "It's fourteen feet tall and seventy-four feet in circumference. It weighs forty tons. It used to be much taller. In 1892, around forty feet were cut off the top to show at the Chicago World's Fair, and souvenir hunters have been chipping at it for a hundred years. They estimate that the living tree was three hundred and fifty feet tall."

We stood and looked at the stony stump. It was curious, but that was all.

"O.K.," Tim said. "Let's go on to the fossil bed."

Scudder's famous fossil bed was even less impressive than the stump. It was not much more than a ditch. It was a wash, a gully, a shallow gulch about fifty feet long worn into the flank of a grass-grown ridge, and we were walking up its dusty floor before I knew what it was. The floor of the bed was rubble, and the walls were crumbling strata of gravel, shale, and rocklike volcanic tuff. The tuff formed the uppermost stratum. There was a crust of it just under the carpet of meadow sod. Then came a foot or two of shale. The rest of the bed was gravel.

Thompson stopped and kicked at a pile of rubble. He picked up a slab of shale about the size of my hand. It was laminated like a piece of plywood in layers of gray, tan, and rusty red. He turned it on edge on a chunk of tuff and tapped a gray layer with the adze-like blade of his hammer. The slab split cleanly apart. He held out two smooth gray faces of shale.

"Nothing," Tim said. "Here's a better-looking piece. Try this."

It was a better piece. Thompson split it apart, and on one of the gray faces was a buckshot scattering of tiny brown specks. They looked like tiny burns.

"What do you think?" he said. "Charcoal?"

"Probably," Tim said. "It might be a bunch of little mosquitoes." He pulled out a magnifying lens and took a closer look. "I guess it's just charcoal, though."

There was another gray grain on the piece of shale. Thompson tapped it in two. He gave a startled grunt, and showed us one of the halves. On it was the imprint of a little leaf.

"Hey," Tim said. "Look at that one."

"Not bad, huh?" Thompson said. "How would you identify it, Tim? It looks a little like birch."

"Or elm," I said.

"It does," Tim said. "But I don't think it's either of those. I don't think it has any modern equivalent. I think it's a shrub they call *Fagopsis longifolia*. It's fairly common in these beds."

"Whatever it is," Thompson said, "it's a real nice specimen."

It was a beautiful specimen. I sat down on a hump of landslidden gravel and examined it with the magnifying glass. It looked like an actual leaf—a dry, brown, fallen autumn leaf. Every detail was perfectly preserved. The leaf stalk was there, and the midrib, and the delicate opposite veins. Only the very tip was missing. It was an almost flawless fossil image. But to me it was more than that. The petrified stump was merely a monstrous relic. This was a recognition.

I remembered a phrase from my reading. It was one of Estella Leopold's apothegms: "Florissant is a window on the Oligocene." The window had opened in my hand, and I was looking in.

We spent an hour and a half in the fossil bed. We found a dozen fossils or fossil fragments—twigs and charcoal, bits of leaves and a fully formed willow leaf, a faint impression of a fly. None of them compared in quality with the little *Fagopsis* leaf, but that was only a disappointment. It didn't really matter. The *Fagopsis* leaf was revelation enough. It was almost two o'clock when we climbed out of the bed and walked back to the house, and long past time for lunch. Thompson and I left Tim at the house. We got a couple of cans of Fresca from a vending machine on the gallery and a bag of diner sandwiches from the car and sat down to lunch in the grass at the edge of the parking lot. We looked out at the sunny sweep of the wild-flower meadows as we ate. They were still wonderfully pretty meadows, but it seemed to me that I saw them differently now. I could see them now for what they really were.

A little distance up the gravel road from the Singer ranch, we came to a gate with a sign: "Pike Petrified Forest." This was the other sequoia-stump concession. We didn't stop. The gate was fastened with a padlock, and we didn't have time to see if anyone was at home. The road ran on through the rolling meadows for another mile or two. Then the land began to rise on the left, and a winding row of hillside houses thrust suddenly into view. A graded road led up from the gravel road through a wide rustic gateway with an arching log-cabin roof. Across the arch stretched a thirty-foot sign: "Colorado Mountain Estates." On the right of the gateway, there was a billboard sign in the shape of a house: "Colorado Mountain Estates. ½ Acre Lots." Beyond the gateway was a street sign: "Arrowhead Lane." We turned up Arrowhead Lane.

"There are two more places that I want you to see," Thompson said. "This development is one of them. There are around a thousand acres here, and they should have been part of the Monument. They're a natural part of the Florissant valley. I can't really blame the original owner of this land for selling. The Monument has been hanging fire too long. But it's a pity. The present boundary line of the Monument is that fence right over there."

"That's pretty close," I said.

"It's a little too close for comfort," he said. "It gives the residents of Colorado Mountain Estates a beautiful view, but it could mean a lot of population pressure, a lot of wear and tear on the Monument. Let's hope we don't lose any more land this way."

"Are there fossil beds in here?" I said.

"I don't know," he said. "But Florissant is all the same geology, so I suppose there are. Or were."

We turned off Arrowhead Lane and drove through Amherst Circle. The houses we passed were cabins or A-frames. They were new but already aging, and they looked cramped and crowded together. Half an acre isn't much land in the mountains. We turned into Badger Circle. The unsold lots between the houses were unspoiled stands of pine. There was a distant view of the farther valley from the top of Badger Circle. A woman with a mop in her hand and a cigarette in her mouth came out of one of the houses. She stood on the porch and shook out her mop and watched us go by. We circled back to Arrowhead Lane by way of Pinewood Road.

We drove back down the valley for about a mile. The road forked there, and the fork on the right was a shortcut back to the highway. We took that fork. It led across the valley, and the land began to rise toward the flanking eastern hills. Just ahead, on each side of the road, were ditchlike excavations. The excavations looked familiar. They looked like well-worked fossil beds.

"That's right," Thompson said. "They're famous, too. The one on the right was opened back in 1880 by the first Princeton expedition, and the other is the University of California bed. But that isn't what I particularly wanted you to see. I came out this way to show you something that has us all in quite a sweat."

The road cut through a stand of aspen and emerged again into meadowland. Thompson slowed the car, swung off on the shoulder, and stopped. There was a ditch at the edge of the shoulder and a barbed-wire fence at the top of the ditch. In the grass near the fence lay a big, shiny twenty-foot length of galvanized sheet-metal piping—a brand-new culvert liner. Just beyond the culvert liner was a parked bulldozer.

"This meadow forms the eastern end of the Monument," Thompson said. "It's part of a tract of around seventeen hundred acres. It used to belong to one of the old Florissant families. A few months ago, they sold it to land developers in Colorado Springs. It was the same old story. It was Colorado Mountain Estates all over again. Except that this time the people behind the Monument—scientists and conservationists and others—went to court. They went before the Circuit Court of Appeals in Denver and came out with a restraining order that temporarily enjoined the owners from building roads or doing any other excavation work. That was only the other day— on July 10th. And the order expires on July 29th. What happens then is hard to say. But that culvert shows you what the syndicate expects."

I left Colorado the following day. Two weeks went by. I watched the New York papers, but there was no mention of the Florissant affair. Then, around the middle of August, I got a letter from a friend in Denver. The letter enclosed a clipping from the Washington bureau of the *Rocky Mountain News*. It read, "The House Monday approved on a voice vote a bill creating the 6,000-acre Florissant Fossil Beds National Monument 35 miles west of Colorado Springs. The bill now goes to the Senate, where approval of technical amendments is expected. The Senate earlier passed a measure identical in substance to the House version. Following anticipated Senate passage, the measure will go to President Nixon for his signature. . . ." The story had no dateline, but the date of issue was printed at the top of the clipping. It was August 5th. That had left a week for the unleashing of the bulldozer. Too bad, but not irreparable. On August 20th, President Nixon signed the bill bringing Florissant under the protection of the National Park Service. A few days later, the bulldozer had vanished and the culvert liner had been hauled away.

# A Natural Miracle

The rough plank table was laid with a white linen cloth with an embroidered monogram, and we sat around it in the dappled shade of a big, yellowed, shedding maple tree. It was almost cool in the moments of sudden shadow, and warm in the shafts of late-summer sun. There were three of us—Alexander Hargrave and Louisa Hargrave and I—and the Hargraves' baby daughter, Anne, pounding on the tray of her high chair. A little black kitten came bounding around the side of the house and across the lawn, leaping and reaching for a wandering butterfly. We watched it come and go, and waved away the hovering yellow sweat bees, and finished our soup. Mrs. Hargrave—dark and tanned and slim in jeans and a thin plaid shirt—gathered up our plates and carried them into the house. She came back with the rest of our lunch—a quiche and a bowl of shiny local Macoun apples. We helped ourselves to the quiche, and Hargrave poured the wine. There were six bottles on the table, all red wine, and all of them open and breathing. Two of the wines were brightly labelled California wines. The others stood anonymous in plain green bottles. They were New York wines—wines that the Hargraves had produced themselves in their forty-four-acre vineyard here on an old potato farm near the village of Cutchogue, on the North Fork of eastern Long Island. The California wines were for comparison. The Hargrave wines were to drink.

Hargrave had filled our glasses from one of his four plain bottles. I picked up my glass and held it into the glancing sunlight. The wine looked dark and heavy, but it had a rosy inner glow. I took a good sip. It was a little hard but not at all unpleasant. I took a bite of quiche. The pie was hot and creamy, with a fragile, flaking crust. I took another sip of wine. I thought it tasted better than the first.

"What are we drinking?" I asked.

Hargrave smiled. "Louisa?"

"Cabernet," she said. "Uh—'74?"

"Right," Hargrave said. He looked across at me. "I thought we'd start at the beginning. This is our 1974 Cabernet Sauvignon—our first wine. And I think it's amazing for its age. Look at that color! It's almost ink-purple already." He took a lingering swallow. "I'd say the tannin is no more than moderate. And the acidity level is pleasing, very pleasing—like a good McIntosh. There's even a taste of fresh fruit in it. It's been breathing, of course, which helps. An hour or two of breathing will improve any young red wine that's honestly made to begin with. But give this wine another year. The color will deepen, the bouquet will develop, everything will become softer—more delicious."

"We used to just drink wine," Mrs. Hargrave said. "But it's so much more interesting now that we're growing our own. There's so much more to understand and look forward to."

Hargrave ate and drank and nodded. "Yes," he said. "But the really amazing thing is that it comes from such young grapes. Our vines are three years old. We didn't buy this place and plant our first vines until the spring of 1973. The exciting thing is, what will we have three years from now? When our vines reach their first maturity."

Mrs. Hargrave swirled the wine in her glass. She watched the rich red ribbons leap to the lip, and then trail slowly down again. "The really amazing thing to me," she said, "is simply what we're doing. There's a mythic quality about growing wine. The vineyard is unique in agriculture. I mean, the grape is the only fruit of nature that has the power of transfiguration. It's as if wheat could turn itself into bread. Wine is mystery—ancient mystery. And I feel that Alex

and I are part of it. We're attending a natural miracle—a miracle
that goes back in time to the beginning."

"That's right," Hargrave said. "That's absolutely true. It gives me
a great satisfaction to have that link with the past. The way we're
doing things here is really very little different from the way they
were done in ancient times. Vergil advises you to cultivate your rows
the width of a horse's hindquarters. I cultivate mine the width of a
tractor. But I don't call that much of a difference."

"Vergil!" I said.

The Hargraves exchanged a smiling glance. Anne leaned forward
in her high chair and gave a corroborative chortle.

"Vergil is one of Alex's heroes," Mrs. Hargrave said. "We pretty
much operate our vineyard on principles set down in the 'Georgics.' "

"Well," Hargrave said. "Louisa is our chemist, our enologist, and
she keeps a copy of Amerine's 'Laboratory Procedures for Enologists'
on her desk in the winery. And I have a copy of Winkler's 'General
Viticulture' and a stack of *Wines and Vines* and Cornell bulletins
in my office. But, yes—I think a lot of Vergil. The 'Georgics' is
full of sensible things. It's a practical manual that also happens to
be great poetry. Vergil trained his vines on elm trees. His phrase is
'wed the vines to elms.' We support ours in the modern way, on
trellises of wood and wire. As a matter of fact, we're more modern
than that. We support our young vines on aluminum stakes. They're
actually unshaped tennis racquets. I have an uncle in Rochester who
makes such things, and I got the idea of asking for his factory rejects.
And, of course, we use fungicides and fertilizers, and Louisa's equipment in the winery is the last word in stainless steel. But that isn't
the point. Vergil is still absolutely sound on the basics."

"Vergil is also great on moral support," Mrs. Hargrave said. "He
has a line, 'Look with favor upon a bold beginning.' We took that
to mean approval of what we were doing."

"It was good advice," Hargrave said.

"Where did you get on to Vergil?" I asked him. "At school?"

"I suppose I read him at some point. But I don't remember it.
My field at Harvard was Oriental studies. I didn't come across the
'Georgics' until we got interested in growing wine."

"What happened to your Oriental studies?"

"Well," he said, "one reason I got away from it was this. My interest in the Orient was in Chinese culture, but I had my degree before I realized that there are very few first-rate American Chinese scholars who don't have Chinese wives to help them with the language. That was in 1969, and by then I'd met an American girl at Smith named Louisa Thomas. And married her."

"Was there another reason?" I said.

"Oh," he said, "I had an operation on my back right after graduation, and I was more or less laid up for almost a year. That gave us time to think. We asked ourselves what would be a fine thing to do in the world. Something worthwhile."

"Something we could do together," Mrs. Hargrave said.

"Yes," he said. "And, luckily, we thought of wine."

Mrs. Hargrave stood up. "Nap time," she said. She lifted Anne from the high chair and set her waveringly on her feet. She turned to go. "Is there anything you want from the house?"

"We could use some clean glasses," Hargrave said. "And my Vergil."

Hargrave picked up one of the bottles of California wine. He looked at the label, put the bottle down, and picked up the other as Mrs. Hargrave returned to the table. "This is a California version of the wine we've been drinking," he said. "Same French rootstock, same Cabernet grape, even the same year. But the grape is only the beginning. The rest is climate and weather and soil. So it's a totally different wine from ours. Not necessarily better or worse. It's a good, honest wine. But different." He poured, and we tasted.

"I think it's a little flat," Mrs. Hargrave said.

"Well," Hargrave said. He shrugged. "We thought about settling in California. We spent a couple of months in California, just travelling around and looking. We saw those endless acres in the Napa Valley. And we drank some lovely wine. But we also heard that some of the newer wineries out there were looking for a cooler climate. So we looked, too. But nothing seemed quite right. Oregon was too wet. Washington was too cold. And California was too hot."

"I remember what I said," Mrs. Hargrave added. "I said, 'Alex, let's just go home and plant a vineyard there.'"

"Home meant upstate New York," Hargrave said. "I come from Rochester, and the Finger Lakes wine country is right next door.

That's where we lived after my operation. One encouraging thing we learned in California was that a small vineyard—thirty or forty acres—was feasible. I guess it was the only encouraging thing. We had decided that if we were going to grow wine we were going to grow the best—vinifera, the French or European grape. The native American grape—the New York grape—is not the best. It has that sweetness, that foxiness. But it is very tough and hardy. It can stand those upstate winters. And vinifera, we very soon learned, can't. Certainly not the reds. One or two people have had some success with whites. But we were really interested only in red wine—in Cabernet Sauvignon, Pinot Noir, Merlot. So we said too bad. It was a nice idea and it might have been fun. Now what? So we came down to Long Island—to Huntington—to spend Thanksgiving with Louisa's parents."

Mrs. Hargrave said, "Don't forget Professor Tomkins."

"Oh," he said. "Oh, yes. John Tomkins is a pomologist at Cornell whom we had consulted. I happened to mention to him that we were spending Thanksgiving on Long Island. That seemed to strike a chord. 'Long Island!' he said. 'There's a big orchardist down there named John Wickham who's been growing vinifera table grapes with good success. He lives in a place called Cutchogue.' He said, 'Maybe you ought to go see him.' So we did."

"We owe Professor Tomkins everything," Mrs. Hargrave said.

"We do," Hargrave said. "That was late November, you know, and when we left Rochester the leaves were long gone and it was winter—real winter. But when we got down here, out here on the North Fork it was still green. Things were still growing. We saw John Wickham, and he showed us his grapes—his vines. They were Red Malaga grapes. It was astonishing. They're a Mediterranean grape—a cold-sensitive grape. There was even new growth on his vines. And there was no mistake about it. He had been doing it for eleven years. Well, if he could grow Malaga, why couldn't we grow Cabernet? It had never been done commercially on Long Island. We could be the first!"

"It was one of the most exciting moments in our life," Mrs. Hargrave said.

"The longer we talked to John Wickham, the better it sounded," Hargrave said. "The Finger Lakes have a growing season of a hundred and sixty-five days. The growing season here is two hundred and ten days. That's an extra month and a half. And the winters here are mild. It rarely gets down to zero. Upstate is frequently fourteen or more below. Everything sounded right—the climate, the weather, even the soil. John Wickham let us see for ourselves. We dug it up and looked. It's a light, sandy loam. It was right in line with the recommendation of a New York State Extension Service bulletin we had. And also with Vergil. That's when I began to pay attention to the 'Georgics.' Just listen to this."

He opened his copy, a rumpled paperback, turned a page or two, turned back, and read:

> But before we plough an unfamiliar patch
> It is well to be informed about the winds,
> About the variations in the sky,
> The native traits and habits of the place,
> What each locale permits, and what denies.
> One place is good for crops, one happier
> With grapes.

He looked up, smiled, and went on:

> Now I shall teach you to distinguish soils.
> If you want looser earth, or more close-packed
> (The latter favors grain, the former wine),
> Inspect the place beforehand, dig a hole
> Quite deep in solid ground, and then replace
> The earth and tamp the crust down with your feet.
> If dirt is lacking, then your soil is loose,
> Most fit for fertile vines.

Hargrave gazed for a moment at what he had read. He closed the book and dropped it beside his plate. "Vergil's 'loose' is what we call 'light'—the sandy loam of the North Fork," he said. "And we had done exactly what he recommended. We had dug a hole and seen for ourselves. We knew we had found the right place. So we started looking. We made the rounds of the real-estate agencies. We read the farm news in the local papers. We drove out from Huntington every few days to inspect some possibility. It took a long time. There aren't that many places on the market. We didn't find this place until April. But it was exactly what we wanted. It was the right size—a total of sixty-six acres. Vergil says, 'Admire a large estate but work a small one.' There was a decent house. A lot of places we saw were just acreage. There was a big potato-storage barn— what they call down here a potato cellar—that would make an excellent winery and wine cellar. The exposure was favorable—a gentle slope to the south. What does Vergil say? 'Southern heights . . . will yield you hardy vineyards full of wine.' And also, 'Your vine slopes must avoid the setting sun.' We kept that very much in mind. Our rows run north and south. Well, we moved in and ordered our vines. We bought the best—registered virus-free, mist-propagated plants from the mother block at the University of California at Davis. We entombed our shoots, as Vergil would say, in May."

Mrs. Hargrave helped herself to another sliver of quiche. "I missed the entombment," she said. "I was up in Rochester, at the university, learning how to make wine. Somebody had to do it. It was either Alex or me—or bring somebody in from outside. But our whole idea was that we would work together. So we chose me. I'd had some chemistry at Smith and liked it. It was really interesting. So was enology. The technique of winemaking isn't really too difficult. So much of it is simply mechanical—handling the equipment. The vital thing is the grape. And then experience—getting the feel of it." She laughed. "It makes me think of something I overheard the other day at the store. There were a couple of men there—weekend people— and one of them was praising the other for the way he cooked his steaks, and he said, 'How long do you cook them?' And the other man said, 'Oh, about two good Scotches.'"

"He must have been from Texas," I said.

"Do Texans drink Scotch?" Hargrave said. "But Louisa's right. There are things that you have to work out for yourself. Where not even Vergil can help you."

"We've been lucky," Mrs. Hargrave said. "We've been lucky in just about everything. We like where we are, and the local people seem to like us. We have two very good friends in the Wickhams. And we have really good neighbors. They're interested in what we're doing, and they've gone out of their way to wish us well from the beginning. They're really friendly. We'll come home from the village and find a pail of clams on the doorstep. Or a flounder. Or, when they're running, a beautiful bluefish. And the house—that was really lucky."

"It was a gift," Hargrave said. "We bought this place for the land—that was the main consideration—and because it included a house. You know, a place to live. We thought it was just a North Fork farmhouse. It looked as if it had been built in maybe the nineteen-forties. Well, my brother Charlie came down from Rochester to help me out while Louisa was away, and after we got our first vines in we started working on the house. It hadn't been lived in for a couple of years, and it needed work. We knocked out some partitions and opened it up. The next thing was the ceiling—a lot of drooping wallboard. We started pulling it down, and all of a sudden we were looking at beautiful hand-hewn beams. Then, on a hunch, we ripped up a section of awful forties flooring. And there were the original wide pine boards. I've made some inquiries, and everything indicates that we've got a nice little eighteenth-century house."

"It could be a really nice house someday," Mrs. Hargrave said. "If we ever get it finished. We're sort of camping out. You saw what the living room looks like. But we're working at it, room by room."

"Farming is hard work," Hargrave said. "Especially in the beginning years. Next year, when we plan to start selling our wine, it will probably be busier. And there's just the three of us—Louisa and Charlie and me. Charlie got interested in what we were doing that first year, and he's a partner in our corporation now. He has his own place here. We three do it all, except at harvest and at pruning time. For pruning, we add two local girls. It was surprising how easily they took to it. When you grow up on a farm, I guess, you learn to read a plant, to understand its ways. It doesn't much matter whether it's potatoes or cauliflower or grapes. And for harvesting we take on four more women."

"They welcome the chance," Mrs. Hargrave said. "Our harvest comes at an important time in cauliflower production. If they weren't picking our grapes, they'd be out in a cauliflower field tying the leaves to blanch the heads. And that is really backbreaking work."

"Charlie and I planted seventeen acres that first year," Hargrave said. "The next year, we planted another seventeen. We have since put in another ten. That gives us a total of forty-four acres in cultivation, with twenty-five acres now bearing. Even so, our last crop yielded twenty-five tons of grapes and four thousand gallons of wine, from about fourteen acres that were bearing fruit. That's an average of about three hundred gallons per acre. Or, as Vergil would figure it, fifty amphorae. We're completely satisfied with that average. I think even Vergil would approve. The average Roman yield would have been sixty-two amphorae for one of our acres. We hope eventually for a total production of around thirty thousand gallons a year. We'll settle for that. It's going to take years to recover our investment. But I think we've got the spirit and the will to do it."

"I *know* we have," Mrs. Hargrave said.

"All we need is the strength," Hargrave said. "There's something in the Bible about 'sitting under your vine and fig tree.' I don't think the writer was a vineyardist. Vergil warns us that the work 'in looking after vines is never finished.' Pruning alone takes a couple of months—winter months, when the potato farmers are all relaxing down in Florida. Listen to Vergil on that!" He opened his book again and read:

> And now, the vineyard sheds its final leaves,
> When freezing north winds shake the glory loose
> From the woods. And even then the country man,
> Keen at heart, extends his care to meet
> The coming year, pursues the vine he has left,
> And pares it back with Saturn's curving knife,
> And prunes it into shape.

Hargrave turned a page. "And this," he said:

> Unless your hoe
> Attacks the weeds unceasingly, unless
> You chase off thieving birds with frightful shouts,
> And prune away the shady darkening growth,
> Unless you pray for rain, in helpless want
> You'll gaze upon a neighbor's teeming store
> And soothe your hunger pangs with forest acorns.

"Of course, there are differences," he said. "We have plenty of thieving birds, but we're spared those frightful shouts. We protect our vines with fine-mesh plastic nets. And we don't often have to pray for rain—not here on eastern Long Island. As a matter of fact, our average rainfall during the harvest months is the same as that of Bordeaux, the home of Cabernet Sauvignon. It's three and a half inches a month."

Mrs. Hargrave finished her wine. She put aside her empty glass and took a clean one. "You know, I think I'd like a little more, Alex," she said. "But not this. It's all right, and I *like* drinking other people's wine. It's really interesting to get a taste of somebody else's vineyard. But let's try some more of our own. Let's try our new Pinot Noir."

"Right," Hargrave said. He picked up a bottle. It was a slope-shouldered bottle of the Burgundy style. He filled his wife's glass, filled one for me, and then one for himself. The wine was lighter than the earlier Cabernet, but the color was brighter and more brilliant. "Well," he said. "Tell us about it, Louisa."

She sipped and swallowed, and smiled.

"I like it," she said.

Hargrave laughed. He sat contentedly back in his chair with his glass in his hand and gazed out across the sunny lawn, on beyond the shadowing maple, to the orderly spread of vines climbing toward the horizon. "It's just fantastic to look at this vineyard," he said. "I'm just overwhelmed. We planted it—and it grew. It's ours. Vergil says, 'What joy it is to sow all Thrace in vines.' I know exactly what he means. I'd like to sow all of Long Island in Cabernet and Pinot Noir and Chardonnay. I've talked a lot about the work, the labor. But the result is worth every hour of it. That first velvety sip of the year's new vine—what a reward! What a magnificent reward!"

# II. The Edibles

# One Hundred Thousand Varieties

I grew up, in Missouri, in the native Presbyterian belief that the tree whose fruit was forbidden to Adam and Eve was an apple tree. I am now inclined to doubt it. So, I understand, are most interested Biblical scholars, but their reasons, which involve such considerations as geography and climatology, are different from mine. My feeling is simply that the apple—the apple I know, the apple of country cider and the autumn roadside bushel—would be out of character in so sinister a role. Toward the end of the novel that bears his name, Huckleberry Finn, another Missourian, approaches a strange farmhouse, and is at once charged by the resident rabble of hounds "a-barking and howling," but he is not in the least alarmed. He merely stops and waits for the bluster to wear itself out and the tails to begin to wag. For Huck, like every countryman, is comfortably aware that "there ain't no harm in a hound, nohow." I see the apple in much the same way. I see it, in fact, as much like a hound— plain, honest, artless, and infinite in its homely variety.

Everything I know about the apple proclaims its ingenuous nature. Even the association of the apple with Adam and Eve and Original Sin can be laid to a kind of innocence. That baleful association was the work of a handful of French and Flemish and German artists in the wilds of medieval and Renaissance Europe—the sculptor Gislebertus of Autun (in "Eve"), Hugo van der Goes (in "The Temptation"), Albrecht Dürer (in "Adam and Eve"), and Lucas Cranach (in *his* "Adam and Eve"). It was altogether their doing, but I can't really blame them for it. I think (inasmuch as the Bible neglects to further identify "the fruit of the tree which is in the midst of the garden") that their defamation of the apple was largely unintentional, for in their time and place the apple was the most easily depicted fruit with which they were familiar.

Literature offers no such sullied history. The poets, in particular, seem always to have understood the apple. It has served them from the beginning of song as a personification of simplicity and goodness. The heartsick Solomon asks, in his wisdom, to be comforted not with some exotic plum or tangerine but "with apples." And here is Chaucer (in "The Romance of the Rose"): "And many homly trees ther were / That peches, coines, and apples beere." And Ben Jonson (in "To Penshurst"): "Some bring a capon, some a rurall cake, / Some nuts, some apples." And Keats (in "To Autumn"): "To bend with apples the moss'd cottage-trees." And Rimbaud (in "Le Bateau Ivre"): "Sweeter than sour apples to children." And Whitman (in "Come Up from the Fields Father"): "Where apples ripe in the orchards hang." And Yeats (in "The Song of Wandering Aengus"): "A glimmering girl with apple blossom in her hair." And Dylan Thomas (in "Fern Hill"): "Now as I was young and easy under the apple boughs." And, perhaps most evocatively pastoral, John Greenleaf Whittier (in "Snow-Bound"):

> And, for the winter fireside meet,
> Between the andirons' straddling feet,
> The mug of cider simmered slow,
> The apples sputtered in a row.

"In its native countries, on the mountains of Chile and Peru, the Potato, in its wild state, is a meagre tubercle, about the size of a Hazelnut," Jean Henri Fabre, the celebrated late-nineteenth-century French entomologist and litterateur, noted. "Man extends the hospitality of his garden to this sorry weed; he plants it in nourishing soil, tends it, waters it, and makes it fruitful with the sweat of his brow. And there, from year to year, the Potato thrives and prospers; it gains in size and nourishing properties, finally becoming a farinaceous tuber the size of our two fists." In *its* native countries, in Pakistan and Afghanistan and elsewhere in the wooded foothills of the western Himalayas, the apple, in its wild state, is a sour and seedy little pome, about the size of a grape. This meagre fruit, an inconspicuous member of the rose family, is known to botanical science as *Malus pumila,* and is the surviving Stone Age prototype of *Malus sylvestris. M. sylvestris* evolved from *M. pumila* in much the same way that the potato tuber evolved from the tubercle. It owes very little to nature. Like the two-fisted modern potato, the apple was largely the creation of man and his selectively hospitable hand. It was also man (with some help from fruit-eating birds) who brought the apple from its original habitat into the rest of the world, and he did so at a very early date. Archeologists are satisfied that it was widely known to Neolithic Europe, and actual evidence in the form of carbonized apples has been found in recently excavated lake dwellings in Switzerland. The science of pomology, which has produced the modern apple of good size and good flavor and almost endless variety, had its beginnings in the early Mediterranean world. Cato the Elder, the distinguished Roman consul and censor of the third pre-Christian century, recorded the availability in his time of seven varieties of apple, and Pliny the Elder, in the first century A.D., listed thirty-six. The Romans, under Julius Caesar, introduced the apple to Britain around 50 B.C. It came to America—North America— with the first European colonists in the early seventeenth century (about the time the potato arrived in Europe), and it there became at once the most American of fruit.

The Americanization of the apple has been as total as the Irishization of the potato. The apple may be as French as Calvados, as German as strudel, and as Swiss as William Tell, but nothing is more American than apple pie. No other fruit—not even the star-spangled blueberry—has approached the apple in its homespun pervasion of American culture. England has its Robin Hood and France has its Roland and Germany has its Pied Piper, but the oldest American folk hero is Johnny Appleseed. No American ever bobbed for oranges, or bought a candy peach at the circus. A man or woman who curries favor with the boss has never been called an apricot-polisher. (The recipient of the annual American Teacher of the Year award traditionally receives from the President of the United States a polished-crystal apple.) Very few victims of the Great Depression sold pears or plums on street corners. Rome is the Eternal City and Stockholm is the Venice of the North, Jerusalem is the Holy City and London is the Smoke, but New York is the Big Apple. Nobody ever said that anything was in cherry-pie order. That—as sure as God made little green apples—would be a lot of applesauce. The Manhattan Telephone Directory lists a man named Grape—Charles Grape. It also lists five Plums and four Melons, four Pears and sixteen Lemons, fifteen Oranges and nearly ninety Cherrys. The Apples (with the Appels, the original English spelling) and their derivatives (Applebaum, Appleby, Appledorf, Applegate, Applegreen, Appleman, Appleton, Applewhaite, Applewhite, Appleyard, Applezweig, etc.) number well over two hundred. And the novelist Kay Boyle has a daughter whose given name is Apple. She is obviously the apple of her mother's eye.

Some years ago, a few days after his wife had given birth to a son, a friend of mine had the happy idea of planting a tree to grow up with the child. Like Isaac Newton and his Universal Law of Gravitation, the notion came to him by way of an apple. He was eating one—a sweet, crisp, shapely Jonathan apple. When he finished it, he saved some of the seeds and planted them in a little flowerpot and watered it and set it on a windowsill in the sun. One of the seeds germinated. A tiny leaf appeared, and then a tiny seedling tree. The little tree flourished and grew. He transplanted it to a larger pot and, finally, to a suitable site outdoors. In its (and his son's) sixth year, the tree produced its first beautiful pink-and-white blossoms. The following year, there were more blossoms, and a couple of them set. Two little green apples formed and developed and ripened. They were recognizably apples, but they were small and sour and nothing at all like their parent Jonathan apple. It was then that my friend inquired and learned the disappointing truth. The Jonathan apple, like every other cultivated apple since before the time of Solomon, is a hybrid, and hybrids never breed true to type from seed. They invariably revert to one of the innumerable other possibilities inherent in their infinite genetic endowment. For reasons still not fully understood, the fruit of this reversion is usually of inferior quality. Hardly one hybrid seedling in a hundred will produce a satisfactory apple, and excellence, though it does occur, is even rarer. Hybrid apples can be precisely propagated only by grafting a branch (or a twig, or even a single bud) from the parent tree to the bole (or even just a limb) of another apple tree.

The hybrid apple came into being (perhaps three thousand years ago) when man was somehow inspired to invent the masterly technique of grafting. This horticultural triumph has enabled him to seize and perpetuate those occasional serendipities that chance throws up from the deeps of the genetic pool. It has also, through these propitious accidents, provided him with apples in a cornucopian variety—a variety unapproached by any other fruit. It is probable that the world has seen the appearance of at least one hundred thousand varieties of acceptably edible apples since the first selected scion was successfully grafted to the first receptive host. More than seven thousand varieties—each possessing some desirable individuality of flavor, color, texture, size, shape, hardiness, durability, or resistance to disease— have been developed in the United States alone. All of them are distinctively different and, to the practiced pomological eye, distinctively American.

The first American apple of which there is any record is the now all but forgotten Roxbury Russet. This is a reddish-brown (or russet) apple that appeared as a volunteer seedling in the village that is now a residential section of Boston. It was found by its discoverer to be an outstanding cider apple. Sweet cider was the Coca-Cola (as hard cider was the beer) of Colonial America, and there is contemporary evidence that Roxbury Russets were grown for that popular purpose in both Massachusetts and Connecticut by about 1650. Two other American apples of superior reputation are generally considered to be of almost equal antiquity. These are a red dessert apple called Fameuse (which had its beginnings in French Canada) and an unusually good keeper called, variously, Yellow Newtown, Newtown Pippin, and Albemarle Pippin. Newtown has been identified as a Long Island village long since absorbed by the Borough of Queens, and Albemarle is a county in Virginia. In Elizabethan usage, a pippin was an eating (as opposed to a cooking) apple. Shallow, in Henry IV, Part II, observes to Falstaff, "Nay, you shall see mine orchard, where, in an arbour, we will eat a last year's pippin of my own graffing." In 1758, Benjamin Franklin, then living in London, imported a supply of Newtown Pippins for his own delectation. Roxbury Russet, Fameuse, and Newtown Pippin all appear, alóng with twenty-nine other apples "worthy of general cultivation," in a report published by the American Pomological Society in 1852. The Society's report for 1915 includes Fameuse and Yellow Newtown (and thirty-odd other varieties), but not Roxbury Russet. The most recent Society report, published in 1974, retains from the seventeenth century only Yellow Newtown. Yellow Newtown is thus the oldest commercial apple in the United States.

Most of the varieties that swell the enormous total of American apples were products of Colonial America. They were, however, very largely mere neighborhood enthusiasms. The great majority of the most distinguished American apples (all, in fact, but three or four) were developed in the nineteenth century. The years before the Civil War were particularly rich in the discovery and propagation of new and exceptional apples, and there was an accompanying rush of interest in the science of pomology. The American Pomological Society ("Devoted to Fruit Variety Improvement") had its inception at a convention of growers in New York City in 1848. The nineteenth century was also the time in which the apple reached deepest into everyday American life. It was the time of John Chapman (1774–1845)—the corporeal Johnny Appleseed—and his half-demented wanderings through the Ohio River Valley with his bottomless bag of seeds scrounged from the dump heap of a Pittsburgh cider mill. It was the time when the apple (whose natural storage life approaches that of the potato) ranked almost as a staple food and (with the banana still far in the future) stood alone as an all but all-season fruit. It was the time when the crank inventor turned his attention from the better mousetrap to the better apple parer: between about 1810 and 1901 (when Sears, Roebuck contrived its definitive Little Star Parer, Corer, and Slicer, with Push Off), the United States Department of Commerce issued well over one hundred patents on mechanical apple parers. It was the time that made James Whitcomb Riley its most popular native poet and "When the Frost Is on the Punkin" one of his most popular poems:

Then your apples all is gethered, and the ones a feller keeps
Is poured around the cellar-floor in red and yeller heaps;
And your cider-makin's over, and your wimmern-folks is through
With their mince and apple-butter . . .

And even Henry James, describing a tour of New Hampshire in
"The American Scene," observed, "One speaks, at the same time,
of the orchards; but there are properly no orchards where half the
countryside shows, all September, the easiest, most familiar sacrifice
to Pomona. The apple-tree, in New England, plays the part of the
olive in Italy. . . . The apples are everywhere and every interval,
every old clearing, an orchard." In 1912, Congress passed, and the
President (William Howard Taft) approved, an act establishing a
set of grade standards for marketed apples. The apple thus became
the first fruit or vegetable in the United States to be subjected to
quality control.

The names of American apples, like the names of American places,
have an incantatory ring. They bring to mind the Painted Posts and
Lost Mule Flats of Stephen Vincent Benét's celebration of American
geography in "American Names," and the stirring sound-track chant
of Pare Lorentz's documentary film "The River." They reflect their
place of origin or the name of their discoverer or some whim or
hope or piety or practicality. They have the sentiment of "Old Folks
at Home" and the exuberance of the tall tale. They have the quality
of resonance:

Baldwin and Winesap and Northern Spy;
Rome Beauty and McIntosh;
Wagener, Wealthy, Gloria Mundi;
Fall Pippin, Ben Davis, and Twenty Ounce.
Milton and Melba and Macoun and Delicious;
Pomme Gris, Wolf River, and Tompkins King;
Bread and Cheese, Pawpaw, and Cranberry Pippin.
Currant and Quince and Pumpkin Sweet;
Winter Banana and Melon and Mason Orange and Olive and Butter;
Arkansas Black, Kentucky Streak, Kansas Keeper, Jersey Sweet, Rhode
  Island Greening, Hubbardston Nonesuch, and Washington Royal.
  Doctor and Piper and Parson and Baker and Porter and Mother and
  Sheriff.

Summer Rose and Grimes Golden and Black Gilliflower and Seek-
No-Further;
Boys Delight, Missing Link, Pine Stump, Sour Bough, Smokehouse,
Hang-On, and Skunk.
Aucuba, Etris, Disharoon, and Batullen.
Falix and Boiken and Zurdel;
Kittageskee, Nickajack, Pewaukee, Cabashea, and Schodack.
Mouse, Primate, Sheep's Nose, Horse; and Maiden Blush.

Some of these reverberant apples have been commemorated, if
not in imperishable verse, at least in durable prose. Ernest Hemingway,
in "The Three-Day Blow," calls up from his youth in Michigan an
apple almost forgotten even then: "The fruit had been picked and
the fall wind blew through the bare trees. Nick stopped and picked
up a Wagener apple from beside the road, shiny in the brown grass
from the rain." In "The Mountain Lion," a novel that recalls the
Colorado of her adolescence, Jean Stafford describes a ranch-house
sitting room: "Everywhere there were small baskets and bowls on
the tables and hanging shelves, full of McIntoshes and Winesaps
and of Golden Grimes." And in his recent Wisconsin memoir, "The
Land Remembers: The Story of a Farm and Its People," Ben Logan
recalls the biggest of all apples: "The wind was still knocking them
down, the big Wolf Rivers, some of them six inches across, making
loud thuds as they landed. Mother liked to joke about those giant
apples. 'Bring me a Wolf River,' she'd say. 'I want to make a pie.' "
A few of the more renowned American apples have been memorial-
ized in the manner usually reserved for the illustrious dead—in monu-
mental stone and bronze. These heroic varieties include the Baldwin,
the McIntosh, the Northern Spy, and the Delicious. The Baldwin,
which originally came to prominence as the Woodpecker, or Pecker,
apple (from the birds that frequented its tree) and later took the
name of its chief promoter, was the first to be so honored. A granite
marker surmounted by a granite apple stands at its native place, near
Lowell, Massachusetts, with an engraved inscription: "THIS PILLAR
erected in 1895 by the RUMFORD HISTORICAL ASSOCIATION incorpo-
rated April 28, 1877, marks the estate where in 1793 SAML. THOMPSON
ESQ while locating the line of the Middlesex Canal discovered the
first Pecker apple tree. Later named the BALDWIN." The McIntosh
takes its famous name from an American nurseryman who came upon

it in a field in Dundas County, Ontario, just across the St. Lawrence River from Massena, New York, in (according to the American Pomological Society) about 1811. A granite monument was erected there by popular subscription in 1912. A bronze plaque reads, "The original MCINTOSH RED apple tree stood about 20 rods north of this spot. It was one of a number of seedlings taken from the border of the clearings and transplanted by John McIntosh in the Year 1796." The Northern Spy (the significance of whose name is a matter of hopeless dispute) is materially immortalized by a pyramidal marker on a farm in Ontario County, New York. It is inscribed "The original Northern Spy apple tree stood about 14 rods south of this spot, in a seedling orchard planted by Heman Chapin about 1800. The Early Joe and Melon apple also originated in this orchard." The Delicious, which has the distinction of being grown in every apple-growing country in the world, is suitably commemorated by a six-thousand-pound-boulder monument in a park in Winterset, Iowa. The monument was dedicated, before a gathering of pomological celebrities, on August 15, 1922. The inscription reads, "To Commemorate the Discovery in Madison County, Iowa, of a Variety of Apple by Jesse Hiatt, A.D. 1872 and Called by Him 'The Hawkeye.' Sole Right to Propagate Acquired by C. M. Stark, A.D. 1894. Introduced and Disseminated Throughout the Apple World as the Delicious Apple." C. M. Stark was the grandson of the founder of the enterprising Missouri nursery that bears his family name. Some twenty years after his acquisition of the apple he so profitably named Delicious, Stark had the further satisfaction of seeing the younger of his two sons display a comparable gumption. This was the late Paul C. Stark, and it was he who tracked down (to a hill farm in Clay County, West Virginia) and bought (for five thousand dollars) and named (as a companion to his father's find) the Golden Delicious apple. That was in 1912, and the Golden has the still unchallenged distinction of being the only important chance seedling apple of the twentieth century. The Golden Delicious has yet to be solidly saluted in stone. Fifteen miles from the Clay County Courthouse, however, there is a plaque, topped by a golden apple, on the spot where the original tree grew.

The apple is the most important tree fruit grown in the temperate regions of the world. It is cultivated wherever the conditions of climate it requires are found or can be provided. These conditions principally include a sunny, well-watered summer of at least one hundred consecutive days without frost, and a comparably seasonable winter. An extended period of dormancy is as necessary to the production of apples as three good months of growing weather. Leaf buds and blossom buds both need an annual rest of at least one thousand hours at temperatures that assure hibernal somnolence. The acceptable range for most varieties is between forty-five degrees above zero and thirty degrees below.

A very considerable part of the continental United States is apple country. Apples can be grown successfully in at least some areas of all the forty-eight contiguous states but Florida. Hawaii, like Florida, has too little winter for apples, and Alaska has too much. At one time, until just after the Second World War, the apple was grown in America wherever it could be made to grow, but an increasingly sophisticated technology has since then made possible an ever-increasing production on an ever-decreasing acreage. The commercial production of apples in the United States is now largely confined to thirty-five states, and the bulk of this production comes from six or seven. Two states—Washington and New York—alone account for almost half the total output. Nevertheless, the United States produces around one hundred and sixty million bushels (almost seven billion pounds) of apples every year, or about one-fifth of the total world crop.

Most of the many apple varieties that were popular in the nineteenth century are still grown in the United States. Very few of them, however, are grown in commercial quantities. Like the home-grown tomato, one or another of these once favored apples may sometimes be found at a roadside stand or in an expensive side-street grocery or on the table of a landed connoisseur, but never at the supermarket. The reasons are much like those that explain the commercial tomato. "Modern commercial apple orcharding, with its emphasis on high yield per acre and efficiency of operations, made necessary by ever increasing costs of production, has been responsible for the great reduction in the number of varieties propagated," Arthur P. French, professor of horticulture at the University of Massachusetts, noted in a monograph. But, he goes on to point out, "Individual varieties do have their faults, which make them unsuitable and therefore unprofitable to grow commercially. Furthermore, with the advent of cold storage and, now, the modern controlled-atmosphere technique, the need for a succession of varieties maturing from early summer to late winter has been greatly reduced." These and other (including even gastronomic) considerations have had the effect of eliminating from commercial production all but a handful of varieties. This handful, moreover, grows smaller every year. In 1964, an American Pomological Society study reported that eighteen varieties were then in significant commercial production. The number now has dropped to thirteen. The five apples so suddenly swept from the general market were the Baldwin, the Wealthy, the Golden Grimes, the Ben Davis, and the Black Twig. In 1915, the Baldwin was the leading American apple. (It is still an excellent apple, but its one fault— biennial bearing—has come to overwhelm its virtues, and the same is generally true of its companions in obsolescence.) The apples currently in commercial vogue are Delicious, Golden Delicious, Rome Beauty, McIntosh, Jonathan, York Imperial, Stayman, Yellow Newtown, Winesap, Cortland, Gravenstein, Northern Spy, and Rhode Island Greening. Five of these—Delicious, Golden Delicious, Rome Beauty, McIntosh, and Jonathan—account for at least two-thirds of the total American apple crop. McIntosh, in 1915, was near the bottom of the list of widely cultivated apples. Delicious, though then in its twenty-first year, wasn't even on it.

The apple, for all its diminished diversity, remains in strong and stable demand. It is still esteemed by most Americans as the meat and potatoes of fruit. Its popularity, though approached by that of the banana and perhaps equalled by that of the orange, is infinitely more broadly based than that of either of these comparatively recent rivals for supermarket preëminence. Practically all bananas are eaten raw, and practically all oranges are consumed as juice. The consumption of apples has no such limitations. The apple is a sufficiently versatile food to command the full resources of the modern kitchen. It is also, to the best of my knowledge, the only fruit to form the subject of a serious, full-length cookbook.

This pomological enthusiasm is the "Apple Kitchen Cook Book" (Popular Library, New York; 1971), by Demetria Taylor. It runs to more than two hundred pages, and (except for an introduction) consists entirely of recipes. Miss Taylor stops short of menu planning, but she plainly implies that the apple can have a natural place in every meal from breakfast (apple juice, apple griddle cakes, coffee) to midnight snack. It is even possible without too much straining to include the apple in every course of a nourishing seven-course dinner. With the help of my wife (and a supply of apples from my own orchard), I have done so. "The crisp, tart tang of apples makes them a perfect base for before-dinner appetizers," Miss Taylor observes, and she offers a choice of twenty-four dips and canapés. My wife and I considered Apple Crabmeat Appetizer, Apple Prosciutto Appetizer, and Guacamole Apple Appetizer, and chose the Apple Prosciutto. Miss Taylor has five soups to recommend ("Fruit soups are not well known in this country, but in Europe, especially among Scandinavians, they are an important item on the menu"), from which we chose Danish Apple Soup. For the fish course, we had a choice among Fluffy Apple Fish Cakes, Apple-Crabmeat Ramekins, and Stuffed Flounder Roll-Ups. We picked the Flounder Roll-Ups. Our choice for the poultry course was Roast Duckling with Apple-Sesame Stuffing. Meat dishes from the Apple Kitchen include meat loafs, meatballs, curries, pies, grills, stews, and a good dozen recipes involving ham and pork. We decided on one of the last—Apple-Crowned Pork Chops. Miss Taylor is more than generous with salads (seventy-five of them), many of which are meals in themselves. We chose her version of the classic Waldorf Salad. Then dessert. The Apple Kitchen reaches its ultimate here. It describes one hundred and eighty-one desserts—from After-Christmas Baked Apples to Finnish Apple Meringue. At Miss Taylor's special urging ("a perfectly scrumptious dessert"), my wife and I chose Applesauce Bowl Cake. Later, if we still had been hungry, we could have had a choice dessert apple—a Northern Spy, perhaps—and a slice of Brie. Fine dining, of course, is more than merely food. It begins and ends with drink. The Apple Kitchen has no bar, but that presented no problem. We began our apple dinner with a round of Jack Rose cocktails—1 jigger Cointreau, 2 jiggers lemon juice, 4½ jiggers applejack. After dinner, with the coffee, we enjoyed a glass of Calvados. Our dinner wine was Boone's Farm Apple Wine.

The popularity of the apple derives from more than the full-course adaptability of its delectable taste and texture. It also springs from a firm and deeply embedded conviction that the apple is a food of almost panacean salubrity. With the exception of the orange (and possibly the prune), the apple is the only fruit that people eat as much for reasons of health as for simple enjoyment, and it stands entirely alone in the reach of its imputed therapeutic powers. An apple a day, the English version of the age-old maxim promises, keeps the doctor away. No other fruit—indeed, no other food—has ever inspired such faith. Nor is that all. Preternatural medicine has never been willing to limit the worth of the apple to the mere prevention of disease. It has looked closer and found it to be aggressively salutary as well. Dioscorides (in the sixth century) considered the apple a specific for diarrhea; John of Gaddeston (in the fourteenth century) prescribed roasted apple as a laxative; John Gerard (in the sixteenth century) reported that the apple, properly applied, could erase the scars of smallpox; "The Queen's Closet Opened" (in the seventeenth century) revealed the apple to be both a cure for tuberculosis and an antidote for melancholy; and Mrs. Lydia Maria Child, in "The American Frugal Housewife" (in the nineteenth century), saw properties in the apple that could thriftily ease a sore throat and inexpensively subdue a stomach ache. More recently, Gayelord Hauser, in "Look Younger, Live Longer" (1950), recommended fresh apple juice for the relief of rheumatism and gout. In "Health Foods and Herbs" (1962), Kathleen Hunter prescribed it for anemia, arthritis, bilious attacks, and blood cleansing. And, more recently, Victor H. Lindlahr, in "You Are What You Eat" (1971), declared that "raw scraped apples are of particular benefit to infants suffering from 'summer complaint.' "

Many foods have been endowed at various times with one or some or all of these beneficent properties. Most, if not all, of them, however, have been outlandish importations, about which anything might be believed. The inclusion of the always commonplace apple in this exotic company is inexplicably contrary to dietary and pharmacological custom. It is also largely lacking in scientific justification. Apples are good to eat, they are an honest and a wholesome food, but there is almost nothing about the apple—no amplitude of vitamins or minerals, no magisterial force or constituent—that distinguishes it from any other fruit. The only vitamin that the apple evolves in more than barely measurable amounts is Vitamin A (ninety units per one hundred grams), and the only such mineral is potassium (one hundred and ten milligrams per one hundred grams), but many other fruits (apricots, bananas, blackberries, cantaloupes, avocados, oranges, plums, peaches, persimmons, pineapples, nectarines, tangerines, raspberries) are far richer in both respects, and the apple's other virtues (a low sodium content, a strong alkalizing effect on the body, and—when eaten raw—a vigorous detergent impact on the teeth) are virtues it shares with almost every other fruit.

And yet, as Dr. Naomi Bluestone, of the New York City Health Department, has noted in a recent issue of the *New England Journal of Medicine*, there are those who "devote themselves to the merciless pursuit of health with amazing fervor . . . uncomplainingly paying 59 cents for one organic apple composted in goat manure and unsprayed with phosphated or carboxylated chemicals."

# A Friend in Disguise

The first real joke I ever heard was about garlic. It went like this:

FIRST MAN: How's that mean dog of yours?
SECOND MAN: Oh, he's much better. I've been feeding him garlic.
FIRST MAN: Garlic?
SECOND MAN: Yes—and now his bark is worse than his bite.

I remember that joke because I was flattered by getting the point. I was eleven years old, and it was my first demanding joke, my first encounter with allusive wit. I had no trouble with the bark-and-bite allusion. I had often heard that at home. Garlic was even more satisfying. This was in Kansas City in the early nineteen-twenties, and in those days in puritan Middle America garlic was not much more than a rumor, but I had heard the rumor. Garlic was repellently foreign; it was French (like snails) or Italian (like eels and squid); it was something like onions ("Don't come near me, I've been eating onions"), only worse—a hundred times worse.

That, of course, was in another world and another time, before the universal triumph of the gourmet cook; and the puritan cuisine has long since yielded and opened to garlic. There is garlic now in every Holiday Inn kitchen, and possibly in every Howard Johnson's.

Caesar salad ("Take three cloves garlic") is on every steak-house menu. A garlic press can be found in almost any hardware store, and garlic bread stands next to whole wheat and rye on the supermarket shelf. It has, indeed, been liberated. The Connecticut horticulturist Adelma Grenier Simmons, in "The Illustrated Herbal Handbook" (1972), concludes her discussion of garlic, "This is such a common seasoning that its uses do not need to be outlined." And yet—nothing really has changed. Garlic has not been much revealed by its emancipation from the back-street spaghetti joint. Like such other commonplaces as sex (in spite of Dr. Reuben) and the common cold (in spite of Vitamin C), it continues to flourish on hearsay.

Almost everything about garlic (including its pungent thrust) is still strangely veiled in rumor. Even its place of origin is a matter of contention. Linnaeus, the great eighteenth-century taxonomist, to whom garlic owes both its classification as a member of the lily family (along with the onion, the leek, and the shallot) and its scientific name of *Allium sativum,* considered it a native of Sicily. The late-nineteenth-century Swiss botanist Alphonse de Candolle, in his "Origine des Plantes Cultivées," seems inclined to favor central Asia as its birthplace. However, he notes the existence of many Keltic, Slav, Greek, and Latin names in garlic lore, and concludes, "To explain this diversity, we must suppose that its original abode extended farther to the west than that known at the present day." More recent authorities are more specifically committed. The editors of the Encyclopaedia Britannica refer to garlic as "a native of middle Asia, west of the Himalayas." Collier's Encyclopedia, the Merit Students Encyclopedia, and the Standard Cyclopedia of Horticulture all describe it as "a native of southern Europe." It is known to the McGraw-Hill Encyclopedia of Science and Technology as an herb "of Asiatic origin." The Encyclopedia Americana pronounces it "probably a native of southern Asia," while the U.S. Department of Agriculture, in one of it *Yearbooks,* judges it a native of "middle Asia." "Fruit and Vegetable Facts and Pointers," a publication of the United Fresh Fruit and Vegetable Association, in Washington, D.C., has an understanding all its own. Garlic, in the Association's pluralistic view, is "a native of western Asia and the Mediterranean area."

Whatever the true nativity of garlic, there can be no doubt that it came early to the attention of man. Its usefulness is noted in the

most ancient records of the most ancient civilizations. So, prophetically, is its capacity for exciting the imagination. The nature of garlic
seems always to have been enlivened by myth. All the oldest cultures—
China, Mesopotamia, Egypt—invested garlic with a multiplicity of
powers. It was relished as food, it was prized as a drug, and it was
feared and respected as magic. The Egyptian records are among the
oldest and the most detailed. The Israelites, wandering in the wilderness, spoke nostalgically of Egyptian garlic. "We remember the fish
which we did eat in Egypt freely," the Book of Numbers records.
"The cucumbers, and the melons, and the leeks, and the onions,
and the garlic." But garlic in Egypt is older than that. When Herodo-
tus made his celebrated tour of Egypt in the fifth pre-Christian century, he paid the usual visit to the Great Pyramid of Cheops, which
most authorities estimate was built around 2600 B.C. "There is an
inscription in Egyptian characters on the pyramid," he reports in
his "Histories," "which records the quantity of radishes, onions, and
garlic consumed by the laborers who constructed it." The importance
of garlic to the earliest Egyptians is most variously depicted by the
Swiss scholar Henry E. Sigerist (1891–1957). Sigerist notes in "Primi-
tive and Archaic Medicine," the first volume of his classic "A History
of Medicine," that "vegetables and fruit were plentiful, particularly
onions, leeks, and garlic." Turning to medicine, he notes that the
ingredients of the recipes contained in Papyrus Chester Beatty, Papyrus Ebers, and others, "in other words the Egyptian materia medica,
consisted of [numerous] substances. . . . Among the vegetables and
spices mentioned very often we find cucumber, onions, leek, garlic."
He then produces a contemporary document that suggests garlic's
supernatural role. The relevant passage begins, "Addressing the de-
mons that threatened a child, the magician said, 'I have made for
him a protective charm against thee, consisting of evil-smelling herbs,
of garlic which is harmful to thee.' "

The early Greeks, like the earliest Israelites, learned about garlic
from Egypt. It came to them first in its most imaginative, or magical,
aspect. Homer, their earliest spokesman, clearly saw it as such. It
makes its appearance in the Odyssey, when Odysseus encounters
Hermes on Circe's hazardous island and the god generously offers
to help him. "Here," says Hermes, plucking a plant from the ground,
"is a drug of real virtue that you must take with you into Circe's

palace to save yourself from disaster. . . . The gods call it moly."
And so, as it happens, do botanists. Moly is *Allium moly*, a variety
of garlic. The later Greeks and their subsequent Roman disciples
saw garlic with somewhat less credulous eyes. If Aristophanes is an
accurate mirror of his time, by the fifth century before Christ garlic
had ceased to be exclusively an instrument of sorcery. He speaks in
his drama "The Peace" of the "excellent commodities which flow
to our markets, fine heads of garlic, early cucumbers, apples." (Alexan-
dre Dumas, in the "Grand Dictionnaire de Cuisine," takes a different
view of the matter. "The Greeks," he notes in his entry on garlic,
"detested it.") Garlic was, however, still thought to possess certain
preternatural properties. Aristophanes, in "The Knights," appears to
regard it as a source of physical courage: "Now bolt down these
cloves of garlic. . . . Well primed with garlic, you will have greater
mettle for the fight." Vergil, four hundred years later, thought of
garlic as a source of physical strength, and recommended it to farmers
at harvest time. Garlic was also admired by Greek and Roman medicine. Hippocrates admitted it to his pharmacopoeia as a sudorific
(or inducer of sweat), a laxative, and a diuretic. To these not unrelated
qualities, Celsus, in the first century, added a capacity for reducing
fever, and his contemporary Dioscorides proposed that garlic was
also capable of expelling intestinal worms. Pliny, a generation later,
struck out on his own and pronounced garlic a cure for tuberculosis.
He also, in his omnibus "Historia Naturalis," had a word of advice
for garlic eaters: "If a man would not have his breath stink with
eating of garlic, let him do no more but take a beetroot roasted in
the embers, and eat it after, it shall extinguish that hot and strong
flavour." Aëtius, the last renowned physician of the Greco-Roman
era, made a final contribution to the materia medica of garlic. Garlic,
he declared, had the power to forestall an attack of gout, particularly
in October.

Garlic declined in medical favor as the twilight of the Middle
Ages deepened. It was too well known in the European kitchen to
compete with the imported pharmaceuticals then increasingly in fashion—the toad sperm, the eunuch fat, the tinctures of sow bugs, the
one-a-day tablets of crocodile dung. There was even a warning against
its use in the influential thirteenth-century "Regimen Sanitatis Salerni-
tanum" as "hurtfull for sight." From time to time, at ever-increasing

intervals, it enjoyed brief revivals. Toward the end of the twelfth century, the Spanish rabbi and physician Maimonides included garlic in one of his many homely remedies for poisonous scorpion bites. The Black Death and subsequent pandemics convinced many physicians of garlic's salvational fumigational powers; one of the secrets in "The Secretes of the Reverend Maister Aleris of Piemount," published in 1568, was a garlicky plague preventive: "Take the top of a rue, a garlic head, or half a quarter of a walnut, and a corn of salt; eat this every morning, continuing for a month together, and be merry and jocund." In the early eighteenth century, when it was widely believed that plague was caused by swarming insects, a company of Irish soldiers survived a visitation (according to a contemporary professor of botany at Cambridge, as reported by the historian C. F. Mullett) "by rubbing their bread with garlic," which "so tainted their breath and the air in their vicinity that the poisonous insects remained aloof." It was not, however, until modern times, until well within living memory, that garlic—with little, if any, encouragement from scientific medicine—recovered almost in full its earlier therapeutic vivacity.

*She came home from her first day at the Cordon Bleu Cooking School and prepared a big pot of garlic soup as a first course for dinner. "Now," she said to her husband as she cleared the soup plates away, "what do I get if the second course is as good as that?"*
    *"My life insurance," he replied.*

The decline of garlic in medical favor was followed, though at a very considerable distance, by a comparable decline in gastronomical favor. It was a curious kind of change. Garlic had been something of a staple food in the ancient world and through the long medieval millennium. The pyramid builders, the wandering Jews, the Athenian market gardeners, the Roman reapers, Chaucer's fourteenth-century Summoner ("Wel loved he garleek . . .") all seem to have eaten garlic as they might eat a turnip or a cucumber—as a vegetable. They probably ate it much in the manner of a Spanish peasant described in "Spain and Morocco" by the nineteenth-century travel writer Henry T. Finck: "At noon he took his lunch, composed of ten raw tomatoes, half a loaf of bread, a piece of raw ham, and a large bulb of garlic consisting of a score of bulblets, which he took one at a time to flavor his portions." Its immemorial acceptance began to weaken around the middle of the sixteenth century. The reason was the birth and burgeoning of the exquisite social fastidiousness that finally reached in Victorianism its withering maturity. Garlic was demoted from a food to a flavor to a mere condiment or spice, and then, at the stricter tables, it was banished altogether. Its banishment was most nearly complete in northern Europe, in Protestant Europe, in England. Shakespeare, in "Henry IV, Part I," lets Hotspur put garlic in its newly obnoxious place:

> Oh, he is as tedious
> As a tired horse, a railing wife,
> Worse than a smoky house. I had rather live
> With cheese and garlic in a windmill, far,
> Than feed on cates and have him talk to me
> In any summer house in Christendom.

In "Measure for Measure," several years later, his feelings were, if anything, stronger: "The Duke . . . would mouth with a beggar, though she smelt brown bread and garlic." The gentlemanly diarist John Evelyn found garlic more odious still. "We absolutely forbid it entrance into our sallets," he wrote in 1699. " 'Tis not for ladies' palats, nor those who court them." Evelyn's strictures were widely heard and almost as widely obeyed. They even, in time, reached France. The eighteenth-century novelist and naturalist Jacques Henri Bernardin de Saint-Pierre, in his "Études de la Nature," alludes to "garlic, the smell of which is so formidable to our fine ladies."

Nevertheless, for all the dread that garlic inspired in the fashionable French, it managed to survive in France, to make its triumphant reappearance in the early nineteenth century in the universally esteemed *haute cuisine*. The sanctuary in which it had passed its years of social obloquy was the now perhaps equally esteemed *cuisine bourgeoise*. Garlic lies very close to the heart of French provincial cooking. In the regions south and east of the Loire, it is practically a kitchen essential. Garlic is, in fact, more generally important in the food of France than it is in the food of Italy, and its stature in France is at least as high as it is in most of Spain. "In times gone by," Louis

Diat, for many years the head chef at the Ritz-Carlton in New York City, once wrote, "the sages divided this world into four elements: earth, air, fire, and water. If these philosophers had been cooks as well, they would have included a fifth element—garlic. For all good cooks, and surely all chefs, would be lost without this pungent vegetable. . . . There is nothing that makes quite the same contribution to an attractive and varied cuisine." Pierre Franey, who as head chef at Le Pavillon succeeded Diat as premier chef in New York, is of the same opinion. "Garlic is as essential to French cooking as wine and cream," he has said. "It is used in making the subtlest sauces— white or brown—of classic French cooking. On the other hand, in many regional dishes the flavor of garlic itself becomes an end in itself." The place of garlic in the food of France (and Italy and Spain and wherever else it is held in high esteem) is thus a solid one. Garlic is not a superficiality of flavor. It is not the French (or Italian or Spanish) equivalent of tomato ketchup or Worcestershire sauce. It is a basic ingredient.

Garlic is a necessary presence in many of the most celebrated dishes in every course (except dessert) on the lengthy menus of both *haute cuisine* and *cuisine bourgeoise*. There are the famous appetizers: *moules à la marinière* (two cloves garlic), *escargots à la bourguignonne* (four cloves garlic), *brandade de morue* (three large cloves garlic). And the soups: *bouillabaisse* (three cloves garlic), *soupe de bramafam* (twelve large cloves garlic), Alsatian chicken bouillon (four cloves garlic). Indeed, as Elizabeth David, in her "French Country Cooking," has noted, "In the southwest of France, particularly in the Périgord district, the soups are nearly always enriched with a mixture of fried vegetables, onion and garlic, called *La Fricassée* or *le hâchis*." At times, she adds, everything is dispensed with except the garlic. The result is then *soupe à l'ail*. There are the fish dishes: *turbot à l'espagnole* (one clove garlic), *homard à l'américaine* (three cloves garlic), *bourride de sole avec sauce aïoli*. (Aïoli is a virile garlic mayonnaise.) There are the monuments of the poultry course: *caneton à l'orange* (two cloves garlic, sliced), *perdrix à la catalane* (twenty-four cloves garlic), *poulet béarnais* (forty cloves garlic). And the meat dishes: *bœuf à la bourguignonne* (two cloves garlic), *gigot d'agneau à la boulangère* (three cloves garlic), oxtail *chez soi* (four cloves garlic). A popular mashed-potato dish in France, *purée de pommes de terre à l'ail*, calls for "2 heads garlic, about 30 cloves," and garlic is one of the traditional components of *sauce vinaigrette*, the classic French salad dressing. Moreover, garlic has an indispensable role in the technology of the French kitchen. The ubiquitous brown earthenware casserole is never used as it comes from the store. It is first rubbed, inside and out, with garlic to toughen it and to remove any taste or smell of clay.

The French appreciation of garlic includes a natural understanding (seemingly denied to many other peoples) of the nature of its so often abominated odor. Garlic expels its most odious breath when— in the manner of Henry T. Finck's Spanish peasant—it is eaten whole and raw. Ford Madox Ford, in a memoir called "Provence," recalls an English mannequin whose un-English craving for garlic jeopardized her job. But garlic, she decided, came first. "So," Ford relates, "she had determined to resign her post, and had gone home and cooked for herself a *poulet béarnais*, the main garniture of which is a kilo— 2 lb—of garlic per chicken." This she devoured for lunch. "Then she set out gloomily towards the place that . . . she must leave forever. Whilst she had been buttoning her gloves she had kissed an old aunt whose protests had usually been as clamant as those of her studio-mates. The old lady had merely complimented her on her looks. At the studio there had been no outcry. . . . She had solved the great problem; she had schooled her organs to assimilate, not to protest against, the sacred herb." Ford was mistaken. His mannequin had solved her problem not by a physiological contortion but by eating her garlic well cooked. The essence of garlic is a volatile oil that is largely released and dissipated by mincing or crushing (as in *sauce vinaigrette*) and (as in *poulet béarnais*) by cooking.

*Two young secretaries for an insurance company were having lunch. One of them had spent the morning checking some mortality statistics. "Did you know that every time I breathe a man dies?" she said.*

*"That's what I've been telling you," the other said. "You shouldn't eat so much garlic."*

The specific principle of garlic is a molecular complexity that also occurs, though in much less ardent form, in onions, leeks, chives, shallots, and other members of the genus *Allium*. This principle is a precursor, or a true mother compound, that is known in the upper reaches of chemistry as S-allyl-L-cysteine sulfoxide or, more conversationally, alliin. Alliin evolves, by enzyme action, a compound known as allylthiosulfinate, or allicin. Allicin, in turn, evolves two substances that together form the volatile oil of garlic. One of these is called allyl disulfide. The other is called allyl thiosulfonate. Allyl disulfide is largely responsible for the taste, the smell, and—when it has been ingested, absorbed into the bloodstream, and expelled from the lungs in respiration—the violent breath of garlic. Allyl thiosulfonate is the active essence whose range of activity—mostly imagined or misunderstood, but real enough in its antibacterial, anthelmintic, and fungicidal powers—brought garlic to more than gastronomical attention.

The scientific explication of garlic began with the establishment of an authoritative organic chemistry around the middle of the nineteenth century. Pasteur found time, in 1858, in the course of his fermentation studies, to examine garlic for possible antiseptic powers. His generally favorable findings, together with the prospect of uncovering other therapeutic qualities, quickened a considerable experimental interest in garlic, and by the turn of the century it was under widespread scientific scrutiny. Its inclusion in the United States Pharmacopoeia seemed imminent. This interest continued through the nineteen-thirties and forties and into the fifties, when (through the efforts of a company of Swiss and American investigators) the pharmacological nature of garlic was finally fully revealed. It was a distinguished scientific achievement, but, in the context of contemporary therapeutics, its results were disappointing. Garlic was returned to the kitchen. A total of only seventy-one scientific papers on biomedical aspects of garlic were published throughout the world in the ten-year period between 1963 and 1973. A lively scientific subject usually produces a hundred or more papers a year.

The hopes that garlic once encouraged in medical science have not entirely vanished. They have merely been abandoned by medicine. Garlic is elsewhere held in high regard. Naturopathy, phytotherapy, and hypochondria all include it in their standard pharmacologies. So does Gaylord Hauser. In "Look Younger, Live Longer," his jubilation of brewer's yeast and blackstrap molasses, first published in 1950, he fixes a favorable eye on garlic. "A friend in disguise," he writes. "Whether you love or hate garlic, the fact remains: it is a very wonderful plant. . . . Digestive disturbances, as gas and colitis, are unknown among the Slavic people, who eat quantities of fresh and dried garlic. . . . The next time your 'inner man' is out of order, make this cream of garlic soup: Cut up 4 cloves of fresh garlic and cook for 5 minutes in a cup of fortified milk. . . . Some garlic enthusiasts claim that this is the best sleep inducer." More recently recruited enthusiasts go considerably further than that in their testimonials for garlic. They tend to credit it with a therapeutic reach that extends from acne to tuberculosis. An English naturopath named Kathleen Hunter is among the more restrained of these garlicophiles. In "Health Foods and Herbs" (1962), she introduces garlic as "Miracle Herb. Diaphoretic, diuretic, and expectorant. One of the most valuable plants in nature. Garlic juice is made into a syrup with honey and given with advantage in coughs, colds, and asthma." Victor H. Lindlahr, a self-styled nutritionist, and author of "You Are What You Eat" (1941), writes of garlic, "Particularly excellent for bacterial diseases of the nose and respiratory tract. Often recommended for patients with high blood pressure. . . . Well-known as a worm remedy. A good source of Vitamin C." And, he adds, "Vitamin C relieves arthritis." In "Nature's Medicines" (1966), Richard Lucas declares that "miraculous healing power appears to exist in common garlic." He then turns the rostrum over to Kristine Nolfi, a Danish physician and naturopath, and author of "My Experiences with Living Food." Dr. Nolfi enumerates: "Garlic has a strengthening and laxative effect, lowers too high blood pressure and raises one which is too low; it also cures indigestion, disinfects the contents of the stomachs of those who lack hydrochloric acid in their gastric juice for this purpose. . . . If one puts a piece of garlic in his mouth, at the onset of a cold, on both sides between cheek and teeth, the cold will disappear within a few hours or, at most, within a day. . . . Garlic makes loose teeth take root again, removes tartar, and has a curative effect on eye catarrh." G. J. Binding, an English admirer, and author of "Everything You Want to Know About Garlic" (1970), takes up where Dr. Nolfi leaves off. "Garlic," he notes, "is ideal for use in all respiratory infections, bronchitis, and asthma . . . a wonderful preventative against tuberculosis, pneumonia, diphtheria, and typhus. Being a great aid to the digestion, it can kill all manner of worms and is a food for the nerves. . . . It has been established that oil of garlic is about one-tenth the strength of penicillin." In addition, he proclaims, garlic is a nourishing food: "It contains a certain amount of protein and calcium, is rich in potassium and phosphorus and has a supply of Vitamins B and C. Taking all this goodness into consideration, we are certainly getting good value for money in the purchase of a bulb of garlic for a few cents." Even France, the heartland of culinary garlic, has its advocates of garlic druggery. The phytotherapist Maurice Mességué, whose patients have included Cocteau, Mistinguett, Pope John XXIII, Utrillo, and King Farouk, is the most celebrated of these. In his autobiographical "Of Men and Plants" (1973), Mességué reports that he has had much success in treating allergies with a decoction of garlic, single-seed hawthorn blossom, greater celandine, couch-grass root, common broom, sage, and linden blossom. In other combinations, he has found garlic effective in the treatment of arteriosclerosis, arthritis, asthma, acne of gastric origin, incontinence of urine, bronchial diseases, emphysema, hypertension, liver diseases, and dyspepsia. These decoctions, however, are not to be taken internally. Mességué restricts his clinical use of garlic and all other herbs to baths—hip, foot, and hand.

For those true believers unable or unwilling to take their garlic in its natural state, either orally or by absorption through the skin, American technology provides an alternative. Pharmaceutical preparations of garlic may be bought at any robust health-food store. The standard preparations include Garlic-Parsley Tablets ("a food supplement"), New Garlee Tablets ("chlorophyllated dehydrated garlic, two tablets after each meal"), and Garlic Oil Perles ("six minims oil of garlic in a base of natural vegetable oils"). All of them carry this statement: "The need for garlic in human nutrition has not been established." The late Eleanor Roosevelt was perhaps the most distinguished member of the company for whom the nutritional need for garlic did not have to be established. She was also a highly fastidious one. It was her custom (she once wrote) to take three perles of garlic oil, each protectively coated with milk chocolate, every morning after breakfast. She did this in the belief that it improved her memory.

FIRST WOMAN: *Why do you feed your children garlic at bedtime?*
SECOND WOMAN: *So we can find them in the dark.*

Science has no such panoramic view of garlic. Garlic, to its narrowed eye, has more to do with the pleasures of the table than with the resources of the medicine cabinet. This is not to deny the antibacterial, anthelmintic, and fungicidal powers of garlic. Moreover, as folk understanding has long insisted, garlic is biologically active against a variety of insect pests. "It would now appear proven beyond all doubt," the Henry Doubleday Research Association, a British horticultural foundation, reported in 1972, at the end of an eight-year study, "that, given certain conditions, essential oil of garlic could be as effective as DDT or similar pesticides, with the advantages of being non-toxic at high concentrations to men and animals, while being lethal to certain pests, especially caterpillars and larvae." Folk experience was, in fact, the immediate inspiration of the Doubleday investigation. "We were induced," the report notes, "to experiment with garlic as a possible insecticide owing to the observation that, when garlic is planted between onion rows, the attacks of the onion fly, *Hylemya antiqua*, are much reduced." Similar studies (in India, in Iran, at the University of California at Davis) have further extended its pesticidal reach. This now embraces thrips, maggots, fungi, mosquitoes, rabbits, and the plum curculio. It should be added, however, that this has not been my own experience. Last summer, I planted a row of carrots between two rows of garlic, and rabbits ate the tops off all my carrots.

The agents of human disease are less susceptible to garlic than are the pests of farm and home. Its antimicrobial powers, though real, are far from masterful. Mr. Binding's modest claim that "oil of garlic is about one-tenth the strength of penicillin" somewhat overstates the case. Chester J. Cavallito and John Hays Bailey, in their paper "Allicin, the Antibacterial Principle of *Allium sativum*," which appeared in the *Journal of the American Chemical Society* in 1944, and which is the classic study in the field, put the matter differently: "By the cylinder-plate method against *Staphylococcus aureus*, allicin shows an activity equivalent to about 15 Oxford penicillin units per milligram, which is about 1% of the activity of penicillin." Other investigators have found its mastery of intestinal worms and fungal infestations to be comparably unexceptional. The nutritional claims that Mr. Binding (among others) advances for garlic are also rather bigger than life. The Agricultural Research Service of the

United States Department of Agriculture, in its handbook "Composition of Foods," offers a truer likeness. By its reckoning, a hundred grams of garlic (a hundred grams being the standard quantity value employed) contain a hundred and thirty-seven calories. Most of this (30.8 grams) is carbohydrate. The protein content is 6.2 milligrams. The most abundant mineral constituents are phosphorus (202 milligrams) and potassium (529 milligrams); ascorbic acid (15 milligrams) is the most abundant vitamin. These are good nutritional values, but they are not impressive bargains. The relative wealth that garlic possesses in potassium and phosphorus and Vitamin C cannot be acquired without effort. One hundred grams is three and a half ounces of garlic, or three large bulbs, or forty or fifty cloves.

It is at this point, with these amiable concessions, that science tends to stiffen. There is no evidence that any larger claims for garlic, either in sickness or in health, have any foundation in demonstrable fact. The remedial vigor that its admirers so variously discern is merely apparent. It is certain that garlic druggery has often been followed by salubrious results. The probability is, however, that these results have had their origin not in garlic but in faith or coincidence, or both. There are few chronic diseases (including tuberculosis, arthritis, gout, asthma, peptic ulcer, malaria, colitis, even leukemia) that are not graced with occasional spontaneous remissions, and it is equally true (as the long survival of the human race attests) that even the most ferociously acute diseases can be on occasion self-limiting, and essentially cure themselves. And faith, of course, is the unfathomable phenomenon known to medicine as the placebo effect.

But a doctor I know said he would hesitate to say that garlic was medically useless. "Take the common cold," he said. "I'm not suggesting that garlic can cure a cold. But it might very well prevent one. Suppose a man ate a clove of garlic after every meal. That would certainly keep the cold-carrying coughers and sneezers a good safe distance away."

# The Humblest Fruit

My grandfather was a country doctor, and in his last years, when I knew him, he liked to talk about his experiences in practice. One story that I remember had to do with a call to a backwoods farmhouse to deliver a baby. It was late afternoon when he got there, and by the time the baby had been born and bathed and swaddled it was night, and the farmer offered to fix him some supper. My grandfather said he thanked him but declined.

"That's right," he told me. "But there were some bananas in a bowl on the kitchen table, and I said if he didn't mind I'd just have one of them."

"A banana!" I said. I was eight or nine years old, and always ready to eat. "That's all you wanted for supper, Grandpa—just an old banana?"

"No, sir," he said. "It wasn't that. I was good and hungry. But I was afraid to eat in that house. I was sure it was crawling with germs. It was filthy. It was the dirtiest house I've ever had to set foot in. Those people were worse than hogs. But now I'll tell you a secret. Bananas are a remarkable fruit. I mean, they are a whole lot more than just good eating. And one of the remarkable things about them is this: They're *safe*—there isn't anything cleaner than a banana sealed inside its skin. Just be sure that you peel it yourself."

Enthusiasm for the banana was a characteristic of my grandfather's generation. His was the first generation in America to become familiarly acquainted with the banana, and it was as much appreciated then as it is taken for granted now. To those who came only a little earlier—the generation that grew up just before the Civil War— the banana, if it was known at all, was a fruit (or was it a vegetable?) as rare as the pomegranate. Practically all those who did know it then were travellers in the hot and steamy lowlands where it most abundantly grows—in South and Central America, in the Caribbean, in West Africa, in Southeast Asia. One of these travellers was the New Orleans-born concert pianist and composer Louis Moreau Gottschalk. Gottschalk, whose compositions include a tribute called "Le Bananier," became attached to the banana during a long sojourn in Cuba in the eighteen-fifties, and he often mentions it in his autobiographical "Notes of a Pianist": ". . . giving a concert wherever I found a piano, sleeping wherever night overtook me—on the grass of the savanna, or under the palm-leaf roof of a *veguero* with whom I partook of a tortilla, coffee, and banana." A *veguero*, he adds, is a tobacco grower and "king of the savanna, who can live the whole year on exquisite bananas, on savory cocoa . . . and the best tobacco in the world."

It is probable that Gottschalk had some slight acquaintance with the banana before he discovered it in Cuba. Bananas were now and then seen in New Orleans markets in the eighteen-thirties and forties, when he was growing up there. Traders sailing from Honduras or Costa Rica would sometimes pile a few bunches on deck and hope to make New Orleans before they ripened and spoiled. The other important American ports—Philadelphia, New York, Boston—were generally considered too distant by even the fastest clipper for even the wildest gamble. As always, however, there was an occasional gambler. The annals of the trade record that in May, 1843, a New York commission merchant named John Pearsall imported three hundred bunches of the russet variety known as Cuban Red, and sold the lot at a price of twenty-five cents a "finger," or single banana. That, since Pearsall was a commission merchant, seems to have been merely the wholesale price. Moreover, twenty-five cents had the value then of over two dollars today. The record also notes that some years later a shipment of three thousand bunches of Cuban Reds reached Pearsall in a state too ripe to be sold at any price, and he declared himself a bankrupt. The banana remained an expensive delicacy through most of the nineteenth century. It was one of the curiosities—along with the telephone—at the Centennial Exposition in Philadelphia in 1876. There bananas were individually wrapped in tinfoil and priced at ten cents (about fifty cents today). As late as the eighteen-nineties, as the Maine novelist Mary Ellen Chase recalls in her memoir of her childhood, "A Goodly Heritage," the banana was still for many Americans a novelty and a treat. She particularly remembers the arrival of the Boston supply schooner at her native Blue Hill Bay one autumn afternoon. "Most remarkable of all her goods in those relatively fruitless days were crates of oranges, two kegs of white grapes, packed in sawdust, and—most wonderful to relate!—a huge bunch of bananas in a long, slatted frame," Miss Chase writes. "It may seem impossible today to wax romantic over a bunch of bananas! But in that huge frame standing on *The Golden Hunter's* deck, behind those masses of brown, tropical grass, were concealed far more than bananas, delectable and desirable as they were in themselves. Therein among those unripe, green protuberances . . . lay a prestige and a pre-eminence among our fellows which in all the years that have passed I have never been able to recapture. My father had bought the bananas as a surprise . . . since the price of them in the village store, at least of enough to supply our family, was prohibitive . . . [and] from that day to this I have never been able to regard a banana with the supercilious stare of the cultivated mind and eye. The munificence and magnanimity of my father, the opulence and distinction of us as a family, remain, always to be evoked by any chance sight of that humblest and ugliest of fruits."

The ugliness (to Miss Chase's otherwise admiring eye) of the banana must be laid to the genetic hand of God, but its humbleness is the work of the United Fruit Company. It was the United Fruit Company that first achieved a constant, year-round flow of high-quality bananas from Latin America to the North American market, thus transforming the banana almost overnight from a luxury fruit into something approaching a staple. This work was begun in Boston in 1899 with the merger of four variously preoccupied enterprises—the Boston Fruit

Company, the Tropical Trading & Transport Company, Ltd., the Colombian Land Company, and the Snyder Banana Company—into a wholly banana-minded United Fruit Company, and it was (for all practical purposes) accomplished with the launching of the S.S. Venus, the first refrigerated produce boat in history, in 1903. In that year, the first of certain record, United Fruit imported from its Latin-American holdings some one and a quarter billion pounds of bananas.

At least two-thirds of the ten billion or more pounds of bananas now marketed around the world every year (including practically all those sold in the United States, Canada, and Western Europe) are grown in the subtropical crescent of mainland and island known in the trade as Middle America. Nevertheless, although there have been chauvinistic attempts to prove it so, the banana is not a native of the Western hemisphere. It came to the West—like Christianity, the written word, and smallpox—as a gift from the East. Most horticultural historians are satisfied that the banana—the large, seedless, usually yellow banana of commerce—was first developed, uncounted millennia ago in the rain forests of Southeast Asia. Edgar Anderson, Engelmann Professor of Botany at Washington University, in St. Louis, noted in a study of domesticated plants, "The cultivated forms [of the banana] certainly originated in cultivation, some of them as hybrids, and the Malay Peninsula seems to be the chief center of origin." The Roman encyclopedist Pliny (23–79 A.D.) appears to have been the first writer to recognizably describe the banana, and in his catch-all "Historia Naturalis" he ascribes to it an Indian origin. "There is [a] tree of India . . . remarkable for the size and sweetness of its fruit, upon which the sages of India live," he reports. "The leaf of this tree resembles in shape the wing of a bird, being three cubits [about five feet] in length and two in breadth. It puts forth its fruit from the bark . . . a single one containing sufficient to satisfy four persons." Pliny's depiction has the further distinction of having given the banana its scientific name. The banana is a member of the botanical genus *Musa* (possibly from *mûz*, the Arabic for banana), and when the eighteenth-century Swedish taxonomist Linnaeus came to classify the common cultivated species, he remembered Pliny's allusion to the sparing diet of the Indian intellectual and named it *Musa sapientum*. *Musa* seems to have brought out the romantic (or the facetious) in Linnaeus. There is a medieval legend that the banana, not the apple, was the fruit with which Eve tempted Adam, and the name that Linnaeus gave to the species of *Musa* commonly known as the plantain commemorates this pretty story. He called it *Musa paradisiaca*. The earliest clearly first-hand observation of *M. sapientum* was set down by a Chinese scholar named Yang Fu in the second century. In a compilation called "Record of Strange Things," he wrote: "*Pa-chiao* has leaves as large as mats. One stem bears several tens of fruits. The fruit has a reddish skin like the color of fire, and when peeled the inside is dark. The pulp is edible and very sweet, like honey or sugar. Four or five of these fruits are enough for a meal. After eating, the flavor lingers on among the teeth."

The toothsome flavor of the banana was probably known only to the peoples of the East until well into the Christian era. Arab traders are usually credited with the introduction of the plant into the gardens of the Middle East and Africa, but, considering the dry lands through which it had to travel, its passage must have been a slow one. It is probable, however, that it had completed the first leg of its journey by around the time of Muhammad, for there is good reason to believe that the legend that places the banana in the Garden of Eden is a Muslim invention. At any rate, the Arab historian Masudi, who died in 956, speaks in his cultural history of the world, "Muruj al-Dhanab," of a traditional Egyptian confection composed of almonds, honey, and bananas. (The bananas of the Middle East were once of some renown, and one of those who testified to their quality was Benjamin Disraeli. In a letter written to his sister from Cairo in 1831, when he was twenty-seven, he exclaimed, "Oh the delicious fruits that we have here and in Syria! Orange gardens miles in extent, citrons, limes, pomegranates; but the most delicious thing in the world is a banana, which is richer than a pineapple.") It was also the Arabs who introduced the banana—along with the slave trade and the itch for ivory—into the immensity of humid black Africa. It immediately flourished there. The Portuguese explorers of the middle fifteenth century found it established as a staple food everywhere along the Guinea Coast—in Gambia, in Sierra Leone, in Liberia. It was there, moreover, that the banana found its almost universal name. The word "banana" derives, by way of the Portuguese, from a variety of West African languages, in which the fruit was variously known as *banna, bana, gbana, abana, funana,* and *banane.*

The ultimate westward passage of the banana was accomplished in no more than a generation. Sometime in the late fifteenth century, it was carried by the appreciative Portuguese from the Guinea Coast to the Canary Islands. The Spaniards found the banana under intensive cultivation there when they added Tenerife, the largest of the islands, to their infant empire in 1496. (Banana cultivation in the Canaries, though dependent upon irrigation, has never slackened, and its plantations are ranked today among the most productive in the world.) The banana sailed across the Atlantic with the Spanish conquest, and, like the first conquistadors, it first established itself in the larger islands of the Caribbean. The circumstances of its importation into America were recorded by a contemporary witness, the Spanish historian Gonzales Fernández de Oviedo y Valdés, who began his career as supervisor of gold smeltings at Santo Domingo in 1514. "This special kind [of fruit]," Oviedo noted in his four-volume "Historia General y Natural de las Indias, Islas y Tierra-Firme del Mar Oceano," "was brought from the Island of Gran Canaria in the year 1516 by the Reverend Father Friar Tomás de Berlanga, of the Order of Predicadores [later Bishop of Panama], to this city of Santo Domingo, whence they spread to the other settlements of this island and to all other islands peopled by Christians. And they have even been carried to the mainland, and in every part they have flourished."

The nature of the banana is as singular as its history and its shape. Its propagation is unlike that of any other fruit. The banana plant is not a tree but a tree-size herb, with a palmlike crown and a fleshy green stalk that can spring from the ground and grow to a height of twenty or thirty, or even forty, feet in little more than a year. Its visible stalk is not a stem but a tubular convolution of its unfurling giant leaves, and its apparent root is not a root but a rhizome. This is a shallow, creeping, tuberous stem that produces a number of progenitive buds, like the eyes of a potato. Much as the potato plant grows from the sprouting seed potato, the banana is grown from planted sections of rhizome. A few weeks after planting, a leafy stalk sprouts from the reproductive bud and begins its laborious simulation of a tree. A truer stalk then appears in the form of a shoot that pushes slowly up through the hollow center of the spiralling shaft of leaves. The shoot emerges at the crown of the plant as a flower

bud, lengthens, droops, and slowly opens into a dozen cascading clus-
ters of tiny blossoms. It is from these blossoms that the banana's
cornucopia of fruit develops. Each female blossom becomes a single
banana, or "finger;" each cluster of from ten to twenty upthrusting
fingers becomes a "hand;" and the whole bouquet becomes the massive
bunch, or "stem," of bananas. The botanically ordained purpose of
the banana plant is to produce a bunch of bananas, and when that
end is achieved its productive life is over. The cultivated plant is
then cut down and a successor shoot takes over.

Bananas, like many other kinds of fruit, are always picked in their
green, or unripened, state. This is not, however, for reasons of market-
ing convenience, as is the case with most other fruits and vegetables.
Gourmet hearsay to the contrary, a banana is not at its best when
freshly picked from the tree. A tree-ripened banana lacks the melting
sweetness and velvety texture for which the store-bought banana is
relished. Bananas ripen properly only after picking. They must, moreover, be picked at a certain stage of maturity. There is a period,
usually set at about three weeks, during which they must be cut in
order to ripen satisfactorily. The distance the banana must travel to
market determines the moment of cutting. Bananas consigned to
the most distant markets are cut on the earliest possible days, for a
day, even a few hours, can be important in their fragile market life.
Few fruits (the strawberry, perhaps, and the raspberry) are more sensitive than the banana to the destructiveness of time.

A picked banana begins at once to ripen. The process cannot be
halted without damage to the fruit, but it can be tactfully retarded.
In this respect, the banana might seem to resemble the apple. Apples
picked for winter storage can be kept for months in a controlled
environment of low temperature (just above freezing) and high humidity (around eighty-five per cent), which produces a physiological stasis
somewhat like hibernation. But the banana is less accommodating
to commerce. A cut banana has a "twilight" life under ideal storage
conditions of about six weeks. It must then be allowed (or encouraged)
to ripen fully, or be discarded. The storage conditions it requires
include sufficient cooling (or heating) to achieve and maintain a constant temperature in the pulp of the fruit of about fifty-six degrees,
a humidity of at least ninety per cent, and a carefully regulated ventilation system, and these are standard on all banana ships, trains, and

trucks. The twilight life of the banana is a curious imitation of life. In his "The Banana: Its History, Cultivation and Place Among Staple Foods," Philip Keep Reynolds, the classic biographer of the fruit, has noted, "The necessity for infinite care in handling a bunch of bananas will be appreciated when it is realized that this fruit, when harvested, is practically a living organism drawing sustenance from its stalk, with sap flowing and tissues changing; that in the ripening process it generates heat within itself; that a few degrees of temperature above or below normal may stimulate too rapid ripening, or cause checked vitality and chill." The demanding nature of the twilight life of the banana was examined in more detail by Harry W. von Loesecke, a United States Department of Agriculture research chemist, in a monograph entitled "Bananas: Chemistry, Physiology, Technology." "The problem of respiration is one of considerable complexity," he observed. "The fruit continues to respire when removed from the tree, evolving carbon dioxide along with ethylene and probably small amounts of volatile esters. Any condition that radically changes this respiratory activity and thereby alters the normal metabolism of the fruit, will have detrimental effects upon its final quality. . . . In general, the trend of respiration is an initial steady, relatively low rate for green, unripe fruit, followed by a rapid rise during the early ripening period. The ripe and overripe fruit show a fairly steady, but usually slowly rising rate until the peel becomes completely brown." It is this stubborn, lifelike respiratory vigor of the cut banana that complicates the immediate, shipboard inhibition of the ripening process. More is required than merely removing the harvested fruit from tropic heat to storage in a properly ordered environment. The several gases emitted by the respiring banana must be expelled from the shipboard storage bays, for they speed up the ripening process. The proper environment of cool, moist, circulating air must be established in the storage bays and then meticulously maintained. Refrigeration must be so pitched that it quickly reduces the field heat of the banana and also counteracts the waves of metabolic heat produced by the living, breathing banana. This heat, in the early stages of cooling, can be of some intensity. Reynolds has estimated that a sixty-thousand-pound cargo of bananas will generate about eight million British thermal units per hour. That is about the equivalent in heat production of burning a third of a ton of coal.

Bananas are ripened commercially in much the same way that they are stored for transportation. There is the same control of temperature and humidity, and the same provision of circulating air. The differences are chiefly that the temperature of the pulp is gently raised from the numbing fifty-six degrees to a more animating fifty-eight to sixty-eight, and the natural emanations of the banana are retained and circulated through the ripening room. The most important of the gases that assist ripening is ethylene. Ethylene is a versatile unsaturated hydrocarbon that occurs in illuminating gas and was once widely used as a general anesthetic in surgery. Its capacity for stimulating the ripening process in bananas (and also in such other produce as tomatoes, apples, and pineapples) is another aspect of its powerful personality. The discovery of ethylene as a natural product of banana metabolism and the demonstration of its role as an autocatalyst in ripening occurred in the late nineteen-twenties, and it was subsequently found that a more precise control of the process could be gained by the use of additional ethylene. A brief exposure of the fruit to ethylene (in a ratio of one cubic foot of gas to every thousand cubic feet of room space) at the start of the ripening process is now standard practice in the trade.

Five commercial-ripening schedules, ranging from four to eight days, are in common use. The shorter the schedule the greater the heat required to bring the fruit to the wanted state of maturity, and the more leisurely schedules are usually thought to produce the best fruit. Bananas are not brought to actual eating ripeness in the ripening room. That would limit their shelf life too severely. They are ripened to the edge of a color state—called No. 4 in the trade—in which the original grassy greenness of the peel has been replaced by a preponderance of yellow. The fruit is then quickly moved to market and continues its ripening on the shelf. At this stage, a banana has about a week of more or less edible life. The lingering green of No. 4 becomes (in No. 5) a mere touch of green at the tips, and that gives way (in No. 6) to an entirely yellow skin. This is followed by the telltale freckling of the final stage (No. 7) of generally acceptable ripeness. Most people (forty per cent) prefer bananas in the green-tip stage, according to a United Fruit Company survey. The second-largest group in the study (thirty-two per cent) favored a fully yellow banana, and the next (seventeen per cent) the greenish No. 4. Only seven per cent of those polled preferred the fully ripened No. 7 banana. The remaining four per cent were people who ate only cooked bananas, and so bought only green or greenish fruit.

The United States consumes more bananas than any other country in the world, and Americans eat more bananas than any other fresh, or unprocessed, fruit. Apples and oranges and grapes, though all of great commercial importance, are now increasingly marketed as cider (or applesauce, apple jelly, apple juice), as frozen orange concentrate, and as wine. In 1971, according to records compiled by the United States Department of Agriculture, Americans ate some four billion one hundred and forty million pounds of bananas—an average of upward of eighteen pounds per person—and all those bananas (except for a trifling few processed for baby food) were bought fresh. The banana is popular primarily because almost everybody likes its delicate, unassertive flavor. (Simone Beck, the great French cook and collaborator of Julia Child, observed in her recent culinary memoir, "Paul Child, the husband of Julia . . . is as fond of bananas as my husband is of chocolate. Just as my husband has a chocolate dessert every night, Paul Child has a banana for breakfast.") But there are other reasons for the popularity of the banana. Bananas are always and everywhere in season (at Denny's Market in Stapleton, Nebraska, and on the breakfast menu of the Ritz-Carlton Hotel in Boston), and they are always (even at the Ritz) the least expensive of fruit. Bananas are, in fact, among the least expensive of all foods. At around nineteen cents a pound, they are cheaper than rice (thirty-six cents a pound) or potatoes (twenty-four cents a pound) or dried black beans (thirty-seven cents a pound), or even the cheapest supermarket bread.

Nevertheless, for all its great and growing popularity, the banana has few genuine admirers. The enthusiasm of its Gottschalks and Disraelis and Chases faded with the proletarian abundance of the twentieth-century banana. Such proprietary ardor is now reserved for the avocado, the mango, and the organically grown tomato. The banana, unlike the grapefruit, or even the commonplace apple, has never been a selection of the Fruit-of-the-Month Club. Its place in current American culture is very much like that of the hot dog and the hamburger. Everybody likes the banana, but nobody takes it seriously. Indeed—after fifty years of show-biz songs ("I Like Bananas

Cause They Ain't Got No Bones" and, of course, "Yes! We Have
No Bananas") and jokes ("You may be a fine, upstanding citizen,
but that makes no difference to a banana peel") and sight gags (Harpo
Marx peeling a zippered banana) and street talk ("She's driving him
bananas")—people are much more inclined to take it with the utmost
lack of seriousness, as the Alfred E. Neuman, the Keystone Cops
and custard pie, the Top Banana of fruit. About the only people
(other than the United Fruit Company and the equally banana-
minded Standard Fruit & Steamship Company) who continue to
take the banana seriously are doctors and nutritionists. The latter
are inclined to take it very seriously. They know it to be a food of
infinite usefulness in a variety of settings—in the nursery and in
the nursing home, in the sickroom and in the obesity clinic, on the
snack bar and at the training table.

The edible portion of a ripe banana of average size is considered
to weigh one hundred grams (or a little over three ounces) and to
contain about eighty-five calories. Three-fourths of its weight (seventy-
four and eight-tenths grams) is water, and most of the rest (twenty-
two and two-tenths grams) is carbohydrate. Its other components
are protein (one and one-tenth grams), ash (eight-tenths of a gram),
crude fibre (six-tenths of a gram), fat (two-tenths of a gram), and
vitamins and minerals. The vitamins evolved by the banana include
A, $B_1$, $B_2$, $B_6$, C, and niacin, and three of these—Vitamin A, Vitamin
$B_6$, and Vitamin C—are present in significant amounts. Bananas
also manufacture a comprehensive range of minerals. They are especially rich in potassium (some three hundred to four hundred and
fifty milligrams per banana) and are well endowed with magnesium
and phosphorus. In addition, they contain useful amounts of calcium,
sulphur, manganese, chlorine, iodine, copper, zinc, and iron, and a
trace (about half a milligram) of sodium. Almost everything about
the constituent chemistry of the banana is nutritionally salubrious.
Even its deficiencies have their salutary side. Its low sodium content
recommends it for low-sodium diets. Its low fat content recommends
it for low-fat diets. Its low protein content (combined with its general
dietetic blandness) recommends it for inclusion in the hypoallergenic
diet of food-allergy victims undergoing diagnostic tests. And its low
caloric value in relation to its bulk (the standard one-hundred-gram

banana has twenty fewer calories than an average serving of cottage cheese), together with a high satiety factor produced by its textural density (which approximates that of an avocado), recommends its use in the management of obesity and as a quickly satisfying, and wholesome, between-meals snack. It is, however, the positive attributes of the banana that most often and most widely recommend its use: its serviceable complement of vitamins (whose values, since bananas are rarely cooked, reach the table undiminished), its relative wealth of the essential (and easily depleted) element potassium, and, most important, its singular endowment of carbohydrate.

The nutritional excellence of the banana is created in the course of the ripening process, and the ripening process is very largely a matter of carbohydrate chemistry. The carbohydrate content of a green banana is approximately twenty-two per cent starch and a fraction of one per cent sugar. Ripening is an enzyme action that reverses this relationship. It converts the starch into sugar and a small quantity of the gelatinating substance known as pectin. A fully ripe banana averages about one per cent starch and twenty-one per cent sugar. Bananas are thus far richer in sugar than apples (fourteen percent) or oranges (twelve per cent) or peaches (nine per cent) or any other fruit. Banana sugar is a consortium of sucrose, dextrose, and levulose. Levulose and dextrose are simple sugars and are quickly absorbed, while sucrose is more complicated in structure and more deliberate in action, but analyses have shown all three to be almost entirely utilizable by the human body. The nature and abundance of its sugars (together with the accompanying pectin and some subtler factors) render the banana of particular service in the treatment of certain gastro-intestinal disorders. One of these is a wasting diarrhea called celiac disease, which principally afflicts children in the first few years of life. Its immediate manifestation is a hypersensitivity to some element in the gluten of wheat flour and other cereals, and its natural consequence is severe malnutrition. Bananas are among the few broadly nourishing carbohydrate foods well tolerated by celiac patients in the early stages of the disease, and it has been suggested that the fruit may in some way actually soften the impact of the disease as well as nourish its victims. The banana is usually the only fresh fruit allowed the peptic-ulcer patient, and it is often the first raw fruit included in the diet of victims of colitis. Bananas are important as a dietary supplement in these diseases because they offer a welcome spectrum of vitamins (especially A and C), minerals, and easily digestible sugars, but they are even more valuable because they are free from both chemical and mechanical irritants. Some investigators are inclined to think that the banana may do more than merely not exacerbate the suffering of the peptic-ulcer sufferer. Their studies seem to indicate that an alkaline residue left by the banana gives it an explicit therapeutic power (much like that of such antacids as aluminum hydroxide) to bind or buffer the inflaming flow of hydrochloric acid. The banana also has a strong supporting role in the management of diabetes. Diabetics on a regime of protamine-zinc insulin (or a combination of protamine, zinc, and regular insulin) are routinely advised to eat a midafternoon or bedtime snack of bananas, usually with cream. This function of the banana is not in conflict with that regularly performed by the orange. It is its counterpart. Oranges are uniquely capable of giving an almost instantaneous lift to a sagging blood-sugar level. The banana, with its unique abundance of slowly metabolized sucrose, has the capacity to provide against just such a dangerous sag.

The dietetic benevolence of the banana is not confined to the special diets of the sick or the sickly. It is equally beneficial in the daily diet of the well. Nutritionists consider the banana a food for the whole of life. It has, indeed, an almost incomparable span of usefulness. It is often the first solid food in the infant's diet, it is a food for boys and girls in the nutritionally trying years of adolescence, it is a food for active youth and sedentary middle age, and it is only too often the last solid food that can be managed by the aged.

But a friend of mine dropped in at a new health-food market on Second Avenue the other day for an appraising look around. He was pleased to find his Deaf Smith peanut butter, from compost-grown peanuts. He found his favorite soybean-oil mayonnaise. He found a carton of Shiloh Farms fertile eggs. He found everything he hoped to find, except bananas. So he spoke to the clerk at the counter.

"Bananas?" the clerk said. "You've got to be kidding. We don't carry that kind of stuff. This is a health store."

# III. The People

# Schönheit Muss Leiden

I recently gave myself the pleasure of a leisurely stay in Hermann, Missouri (pop. 2,658), an old German town on the rolling south bank of the Missouri River, some eighty miles west of St. Louis. Hermann takes its name from a Germanic hero of the first century and was founded in 1837, on a site chosen for its reputed resemblance to the Fatherland, by the Deutsche Ansiedlungs Gesellschaft zu Philadelphia (German Settlement Society of Philadelphia), an organization created in 1836 by a group of Pennsylvania German-Americans for the purpose of establishing a settlement that would perpetuate German culture and the German language on the free American frontier—a settlement that would be "characteristically German in every particular." By 1839, the settlement had grown from a huddle of log cabins to a town—a flourishing town, laid out on a formal urban plan, with ninety houses, five stores, two hotels, and a post office, and with a population of almost five hundred. Three years later, in 1842, Hermann was designated ("for certain material returns," according to the chief local historian) the seat of Gasconade County. It became a thriving river port ("During those days," a contemporary memoirist has noted, "we were never out of sight of steamboat smoke"), a center of viticulture (for several decades it had the second-largest winery in the United States), and, in 1854, a regular stop on the infant railroad that grew into the Missouri Pacific. There was talk that Hermann might come to rival St. Louis as the trans-Mississippi metropolis. It remained a town. It has never even been more of a town than it is today. It has, in fact, scarcely changed at all from the town of its original eminence. Much of Hermann still looks as it did around the time of the Civil War, and it is still almost as solidly and determinedly German.

The municipal street-corner trash cans in Hermann are labelled "SCHUND," and customers leaving Hillebrand's, the largest restaurant in town, are confronted by a valediction inscribed on the vestibule wall: *"Auf Wiedersehen. Kommen Sie Bald Wieder."* The former mayor of Hermann (until last year) still carries business cards reading "C. M. (Cap) Bassman. Herr Burgermeister."

Hermann sits sheltered in a small, semicircular valley, whose half-encircling slopes were once dense with terraced vineyards. It consists of twenty or thirty crowded, tree-lined blocks of well-scrubbed stoops and old brick sidewalks, and a wide main street called Market Street. Market Street begins at the river, at a narrow iron-truss bridge (built in 1929 to replace an 1880 ferry), and it extends southward perhaps a mile to the first rise of the enclosing hills, where it shrinks to a two-lane road. Market Street has always been the main street of Hermann. It was named, by the founding Philadelphia Gesellschaft, for its Philadelphia counterpart, and it was designed by them on a scale of considerable grandeur. They stipulated that Hermann's principal street be one hundred and twenty feet wide from curb to curb— or ten feet wider than the Philadelphia original. I never got around to pacing it off, but it looks at least that wide. Parking on Market Street is angle parking, and there is still ample room for four lanes of traffic. Near the southern end of Market Street, there was at one time, around the turn of the century, a big square market building, called the Markt Haus, with two rows of produce stalls and a wagon lane between, in the middle of the street; there is now a park two blocks long—with a bandstand, lawns and benches, and an imposing two-story building (until recently the only firehouse and now also the town marshal's office and the municipal jail)—islanded at the northern end of it. The other streets in Hermann are less aggressively proportioned, but they, too, bear the mark of its Philadelphia founders. The distant Gesellschaft required that the streets intersecting Market Street be identified (in the then popular American innovation) by numbers. They elected, however, to give names to the streets running parallel to Market Street. The names they chose suggest some careful thought—Gellert, Franklin, Gutenberg, Schiller, Washington, Mozart, Jefferson, and Goethe. The only street that the original settlers managed to name themselves is Wharf Street.

"That isn't exactly right," J. J. Graf, editor and publisher of the weekly Hermann *Advertiser-Courier* (an offshoot of the *Hermanner Volksblatt*), told me, "although nobody seems to know it. I mean about those street names. Back in the old Prohibition days, the federal agents arrested a fellow here who had a place on First Street. But they had to let him go. The warrant naturally gave his address as First Street. So his lawyer got out the town charter and showed the court there was no such street. The Gesellschaft had named it Front Street."

Hermann is a substantial town for a town of twenty-six hundred people. It has amenities not often found in towns two or three times as large. It has a ten-acre City Park, with tennis courts, playing fields, picnic grounds, a swimming pool, and a handsome octagonal theatre, used for amateur entertainments. It has a modern hospital—the Hermann Area District Hospital—with forty-six beds. It has two medical doctors, two osteopathic doctors (Missouri is the birthplace of osteopathy), two chiropractors, two optometrists, four dentists, and a podiatrist. It has two funeral homes (Toedtmann & Grosse and Herman Blumer) and the Frene Valley Nursing Home. It has five lawyers, a tax accountant, and the Kallmeyer-Schroff Auctioneering Service. It has a well-stocked public library (among the bumper stickers that I saw around town was one that read "Follow Me to the Library") and a movie theatre, the Showboat, with screenings four nights a week. It has the Stone Hill Winery, a recent revival of the relished past, with an average annual production of around forty-five thousand gallons. It has Van Kamp's Boutique & Antiques, the Sound Shoppe, and Klott's Blacksmith Shop. It has a Ford agency, a Chevrolet agency, a Chrysler-Plymouth agency, a Buick agency, a Dodge agency, and a John Deere agency. It has Rohlfing's Greenhouse and the Noelke Jewelry Store. It has the Hermann Cleaners and two laundries—the Helpee-Selfee and the Schillerstrasse. It has a Florsheim Shoe Company factory, a toy factory, and the Hermann Boat Works, home of the Dixie Devil. It has a pool hall (Snake's) and a bowling alley. It has the Sausage Shoppe ("50 Different Types of Cheeses and Sausages") and Schulte's Bakery: *lebkuchen, springerli, stollen, pfeffernüsse, schnitzbrot, streusel.* It has ten beauty parlors, four barbershops, seven bars and the Levee House Cocktail Lounge, and two liquor stores. It also has a resident celebrity—Ken Boyer, the former St. Louis Cardinals star.

"One thing we haven't got," former Mayor (or Burgermeister) Bassman told me, "is an Alcoholics Anonymous. We may be the only town of our size that hasn't. We just don't have that many drunks. Our people are used to Old World gracious living. They grew up drinking beer or wine with their meals. We don't have any kind of extremes. We've got very few people on welfare, and we don't have what I'd call real wealth. I'll admit old Bill Schlender gave us a surprise. Bill was a widower here who died a couple of years ago. He had a shoe store on Schiller Street for as long as I can remember, and he lived upstairs. He wore the same overcoat for forty years, and he used to sit out front of his store in the evening and read the paper by the light of a street lamp to save electricity. Well, he died and left an estate of seven hundred thousand dollars. Including eighty thousand dollars in a checking account."

Hermann, small as it is, has two distinct (to local eyes) business districts. One of these is the two blocks on Market Street between Third Street and Fifth, with an extension along East Fourth Street between Market and Schiller. The other is East First (or Front) Street between Schiller and Gutenberg. The First Street block is known to Hermannites as Downtown. Market Street and the East Fourth Street block are Uptown. Uptown has Jay's IGA Food Liner, the Sharp Corner Tavern (where at ten o'clock one morning, a day or two after my talk with Bassman, I saw through the open door three gracious livers standing at the bar), the S & S Variety Store, and Schulte's Bakery. Downtown has the Riverfront Bi-Rite Market, the Concert Hall Bar & Barrell, Berlener's Rexall Drugs, and the Sausage Shoppe. The First Missouri Bank of Gasconade County, the only bank in the area, occupies a classically columned limestone building on East First Street, but it also has a branch office in a recently restored brick residence (dating from 1871) on Market Street at Third. "We have a strong feeling about Old Hermann," Robert C. Kirchhofer, the president of the First Missouri, told me. "But we don't believe in shrines and monuments. We believe in preservation for use. This is largely why the bank took over the old Reiff House. That was in 1972, and I think it's turned out well." He laughed. "I dropped in a few weeks after our opening to see how things were going, and on the way out I met an old lady I've known all my life, and she grabbed me by the hand. 'Oh, Robert,' she said. 'I'm just thrilled about your new bank. Now I don't have to go all the way downtown anymore.'"

Some people are inclined to think of Schiller Street between East Fourth and East First as a kind of midtown. Most of Hermann's beauty parlors are concentrated there—the Beauty Bar, Jane's Beauty Salon, Ruthie's Salon of Beauty, Marilyn's Beauty Salon, and Gloria's Beauty Salon. Gloria is Mrs. Gloria Bruckerhoff. Her shop is situated in a low, unrestored brick building (circa 1856) that is also her home. "I guess there *are* a lot of us girls," she told me, "but we get along together real fine. There's plenty of customers to go round. The ladies here in Hermann care about the way they look. They're conservative. They still like to wear it teased. I try to keep up with things at the shows in St. Louis, but we're always about two years behind. Another funny thing is the way all of us girls have started doing boy haircuts. I mean for boys. I've got boy customers from two to ninety. The barbers don't like it, but it's their own fool fault. The boys come to me because I'll style their hair the way they want it styled. They say the barbers won't listen—they just keep cutting it in the regular barber way. If you ask me, the boys around here are even more particular than the ladies. I'm even beginning to do those his-and-hers permanents."

The architectural antiquity of much of Hermann is formally and officially acknowledged. In 1972, some twenty square blocks of the town, including all its business streets, were accepted for inclusion in the National Register of Historic Places, Office of Archeology and Historic Preservation, of the National Park Service, Department of the Interior, in Washington. This recognition was largely brought about by the concerted efforts of a number of local groups—the Brush and Palette Club, Historic Hermann, Inc., the Hermann Chamber of Commerce, the First Missouri Bank. "I'm sure it was worth it," Mrs. Anna Hesse, an art teacher and the founder of the Brush and Palette Club, told me. I was sitting with Mrs. Hesse—and with Mrs. William Coe and Mrs. Laura Graf (a cousin of the newspaper publisher), both founding members of Historic Hermann—on the terrace of Mrs. Hesse's home on a slope overlooking the red and green and gray pitched roofs of Hermann. "But, oh, my Lord, the miles and miles of correspondence!" she went on. "I guess you could say that it all began when we organized our first annual Maifest. That was way back in 1952. As you may know, the Maifest is one of the oldest of the German spring festivals. Well, we wanted to try to raise some money to save the Rotunda. That's the octagonal theatre in City Park. Of course, the Maifest goes back to the very beginning of Hermann. But it was originally a children's affair—a close-of-school celebration. I remember—and this was back in the twenties—we'd march from the old German School, on Schiller Street, out to the park, and there would be the town band and sack races and a maypole. And then we'd have the picnic."

"The *treat,*" Mrs. Coe said. "We always called it the treat. But everything was very disciplined. Hermann was totally German in those days, and all of us children spoke German before we learned English. I'm only a Coe by marriage—my maiden name was Dietzel. But about the treat. We would all line up and the bugler would blow a special call and we would march—very correctly—over to the table, and they would give each of us a big slice of knockwurst on a bun. Delicious! Then we'd march away, and in a few minutes the bugle would blow again, and off we'd go to the table once more. This time, they would give us a glass of pink lemonade. And the pink was *wine!* Oh, my! Then one more bugle call, and we'd each get an orange. We really looked forward to the Maifest. But they dropped it twenty years or more ago. It got so the children didn't think it was much of a treat anymore."

"I know," Mrs. Hesse said. "I know. But the Maifest that Hermann is so famous for now is a total community effort. It lasts only two days—a Saturday and Sunday toward the end of May—but it takes months of preparation, and almost everybody in town participates. We usually put on an original historical musical at the Rotunda— usually written by Mimi Schmidt. We have a walking tour of Old Hermann, and a tour of several of our most historic homes, and various arts-and-crafts exhibitions, and a parade, and a tasting tour of the Stone Hill Winery, and we set up beer gardens, and there are concerts of old German folk songs, and so on. We've been a great success from the start. Our first Maifest was so successful it was almost a disaster. We did just too good a job promoting it around the state. I don't know what we expected in the way of attendance, but forty thousand people showed up. *Forty thousand!* And something like twenty thousand cars. There was no traffic control. Our police force is only three officers and the marshal. People drove into town from all directions and parked just any old where. Nobody could move. There were cars backed up for miles across the bridge. Market Street was a solid mass of pushing and shoving humanity. I know— I got stranded there. And everybody was starving. Every eating place in town ran out of food early Saturday afternoon. We didn't know whether to call the Red Cross or the Highway Patrol. I called the Highway Patrol, and at first they wouldn't believe me. They just laughed. I understand that all the way to St. Louis people were taking in strangers and giving them something to eat. It was awful, but we made money—enough to restore the Rotunda, and more. And the next year we were prepared. Everybody in town made sandwiches and set up stands. And practically everybody who came that year brought their own food."

"It's different now," Mrs. Coe said. "We know what to expect. We import enough extra policemen. Everything is organized and controlled. Everybody has a wonderful time. It's been a great thing for Hermann."

"I think it's been our salvation," Mrs. Hesse said. "Hermann would be very different now if we hadn't called attention to our historical treasures. They're what bring so many visitors to the Maifest—our beautiful old homes, our unique living past. And we got started in the very nick of time. The war was just over and prosperity was beginning. The bulldozer was looming. But most of our best architecture was still here, and it could still be saved. What had preserved it for so long, of course, was the Depression. *Our* Depression. We had the longest and the worst of anybody. You might say it began with the First World War. A lot of people don't realize it, but that was the *really* anti-German war. I remember my parents talking. We Hermannites were practically ostracized. We weren't considered German-Americans—we were Germans. We were the enemy. You may have heard of a village near here called Pershing. Well, its original name was Potsdam. Then, after the war, came Prohibition. And the principal economy of Hermann was wine! Almost everybody here grew grapes for either Stone Hill or Sohns. And we also had two distilleries and a big brewery. Then came the general Depression. I don't know how we survived. Those were terrible years for Hermann. But they did have a kind of silver lining. Hard times kept Hermann a nineteenth-century town. They kept it from going modern, like so many American towns. In a way, they preserved our heritage."

"*Schönheit muss leiden,*" Mrs. Graf said.

Mrs. Hesse laughed. "Yes," she said. " 'To be beautiful one must suffer.' "

"Anna's right about those years," Dr. Joseph F. Schmidt, one of the town's two optometrists, told me. "I came here in the late thirties from Washington, Missouri, which has a big German community itself, but I could see the difference: Nothing had changed in Hermann for at least twenty years. I remember a conversation I overheard on the street one day. I'll never forget it. It was two old women talking. It went like this:

"First woman: 'Call me up. I have now the telephone.'

"Second woman: *'Ja? Was ist deine Nummer?'*

"First woman: *'Lass mal denken.* Is it 238? Or is it 382? You got to get it just right, you know, or it don't work.' "

Hermann has two motels, one at each end of town, and two hotels: the Central Hotel (a second-floor hotel next door to the Sharp Corner Tavern) and the German Haus. I stayed at the German Haus. It occupies a building (put up in 1847) that was first a store and warehouse and then a private residence. It was remodelled into a hostelry in 1962. It is a rectangular building, two good stories in height, and built of the warm, salmony brick that distinguishes most pre-Civil War architecture in Hermann. Its windows are long and gently arched and hung with dark-green shutters, and it has the steeply pitched standing-seam iron roof of the period, painted barn red. A gallery, reached by an outside staircase, runs along the front and one side of the building. The office of the German Haus, and the living quarters of the owners, Mr. and Mrs. Van Moore, are in an adjacent building, across a gravelled parking lot. This building (1841) was the first *Erholungshalle*, or theatre, in Hermann. The office is a comfortable room, always open to guests, with a big round table, a circle of chairs, an electric coffee urn, and three freshly home-baked cakes (usually a pound cake, a crumb cake, and a chocolate layer cake) to choose from every day. On the wall above the coffee urn is an elaborately framed poem, hand-lettered in gold foil on black glass and headed *"Göttlichen Haussegen."* It reads:

> *Wo Glaube da Liebe,*
> *Wo Liebe da Friede,*
> *Wo Friede da Segen,*
> *Wo Segen da Gott—*
> *Wo Gott keine Not.*

Mrs. Moore (née Gellhausen) provided me with a translation:

> Where there is belief, there is love,
> Where there is love, there is peace,
> Where there is peace, there is joy,
> Where there is joy, there is God—
> Where there is God, there is no want.

The German Haus is conveniently and attractively situated. It stands on a knoll on East Second Street, a block up from the bridge and the river, and it faces down the boulevard sweep of Market Street. I had a big, high-ceilinged corner room that opened on the front gallery, and I liked to sit out there on an old slatted bench in the late afternoon, with much of Hermann spread out around me.

Off to the right, to the south and west, rose the red brick battlements of the two oldest churches—the Gothic spired and dormered St. George Roman Catholic Church and the Protestant St. Paul United Church of Christ, with its seven-story campanile—each on its own imposing hilltop. ("That was no accident," the Reverend

Mr. Armin Klemme, pastor of the United Church, told me. "Our two denominations were quite competitive in the early days, and the founding fathers planned with that unfortunate fact in mind. They went to infinite trouble to choose for our churches two sites that had practically the same elevation.") Off to the left, on a bluff above the river, rose the red brick bulk of the Gasconade County Courthouse (the gift, in 1897, of a Hermannite named Charles D. Eitzen), with its colonnaded porch, its four corner domes, and its great central silvery dome ablaze in the setting sun. I could even see, if I stood and craned my neck, the little green bronze cannon (a six-pounder cast in Boston) on its limestone mounting on the courthouse lawn. ("Cannons had names in those old days," Arthur A. Schweighauser, a retired vice-president of the Laclede Steel Company, in St. Louis, and president of Historic Hermann, told me. "Ours is named Ever True. Ever True fired three shots in the Civil War. This is ultra-Republican country, as I suppose you know, and it has been since the beginning. Gasconade County and St. Louis County were the only two counties in Missouri that voted for Lincoln in 1860. So we were on the Union side, and Ever True has the distinction of having stopped the advance of General Sterling Price's Confederate Army for almost half an hour. That was in October of 1864. There was nobody living in Hermann then but women and children and a few old men—the rest of the men were off fighting for the Union. Price's cavalry commander, General Marmaduke, knew that. So he came riding up the river toward what turned out to be the terrible Battle of Westport, near Kansas City, feeling nice and relaxed. Then, all of a sudden, there was a cannon shot from somewhere up in town. Marmaduke thought he was being bushwhacked. He stopped and waited, and a few minutes later there was another shot, this time from a different point in town. Then came another shot, from still another point. But after that, no more. Marmaduke sent out a party of scouts. They brought back the answer: a few old men had been carrying Ever True from hill to hill and pretending to be an army. Well, Marmaduke had his men throw Ever True into the river. But after he left we fished it out. We don't claim a victory, of course. I think Price would probably have been defeated at Westport even without our help.") I could also see, around one end of the gallery, the superstructure of the bridge and a stretch of muddy river and, once in a while, a little white towboat creeping along with its acreage of barges thrusting out ahead.

But the other view is the view I usually see when I remember my stay in Hermann. That was the view, framed in sweet gums and maples, down the peaceful length of Market Street, across the little bridge that spans a wandering stream called Frene Creek, and beyond—to the cupolaed Stone Hill Winery (built in 1869), massive on its distant hill, and the long green slope and sheltering cedars of the Protestant Cemetery lifting to the opposite far horizon. And I always remember it with the scent of lilacs in the early-evening air and the sound across the rooftops of the bell in the tower of the old German School (now the City Hall) ringing the hours.

I had been in Hermann almost a week before I crossed the Frene Creek bridge and climbed the slope of the Protestant Cemetery. I went, that first time, at the suggestion of Arthur Schweighauser. "I'm sure you've come across the name of George F. Bayer," he told me. "You might call him the founder of Hermann. Bayer was general agent for the Gesellschaft. The Gesellschaft selected the site of Hermann, and Bayer bought the land it was built on. But unless you've read pretty deep, you wouldn't know the rest of the story. The first settlers here had a very hard time for a year or two. They didn't like the land or anything about it, and they blamed it all on Bayer. They made him the scapegoat; they hated him. And Bayer took it to heart. He came down with the fever and died, in 1839. You'll find his grave in the far southeastern corner of the cemetery. It's up there all by itself. When they buried him, the people decided that there would never be another grave within fifty feet of his. Go up and see for yourself."

I found Bayer's grave without any trouble. It is in the highest, most commanding corner of the cemetery, but it is conspicuous only in its pariah isolation. It is marked by a limestone slab, darkly weathered and slumped askew, with his name, the dates of his birth and death, and a carving in relief of two clasped hands. It was eerie in its reticence. And, in the circumstances, it was hard to imagine what the handclasp signified. I moved away, and was stopped by Bayer's nearest neighbor—a three-foot column surmounted by a sundial. It commemorated a more familiar tragedy: "In memory of the early pioneers who perished in the explosion of the steamboat 'Big Hatchie' at the wharf at Hermann in 1842, the thirty-five dead that lie buried here in unmarked graves and the many whose bodies were never recovered from the waters of the Missouri River."

I started back down the slope to the street below, where I had left my car. It took me almost an hour to get there; I had forgotten the strange enchantment of an old cemetery. Death was taken seriously in America in the nineteenth century. Its presence was accepted and respected, and, with their stylized conjurations of redemption, the placatory memorials it inspired are works of dignity and art. The Protestant Cemetery in Hermann is more enchanting than most. Hermann in the years before and long after the Civil War was blessed with a succession of gifted stone-carvers. Examples of their work are everywhere on the upper, older slopes of the cemetery—a dove in flight toward a heavenly crown, an angel kneeling in prayer, a woman bowed and weeping, a lamb beneath a weeping-willow tree, a skull and crossed bones, a finger (with the legend *"Im Himmel"*) pointing upward, an urn draped with a fringed and tasselled cloth, a ten-foot column rising to a pinnacle cone wreathed in an elaboration, in full relief, of ferns and primroses and lilies. Most of the most richly sculptured stones are also inscribed with richly fervent sentiments. I made a note of one:

Hier
ruhen die irdischen Überreste
von
WILH. DORNER
Geboren
zu Langenwinkel in Baden
Dec. 25, 1807
Gestorben
April 27, 1859
als treuer Jugendlehrer
verband er mit grossem
Lehrertalent, Freiheitsstreben, Redlichkeit
und Biedersein, Friede seiner Asche
I H S

Just below a path that divides the oldest graves from the rest of the cemetery, I came across the plot of a family named Heck. It contained three headstones, two of them placed side by side. The first of these was inscribed

Vater

KARL HECK

geb. 25 Dec., 1821

gest. 20 April, 1915

The second read

Mutter

HENRIETTE HECK

geb. GUENTHER

geb. 28 Juni 1828

gest. 1 Aug. 1901

At the bottom of each stone was inscribed *"In Leben und Tod vereint."* But what interested me was the third stone. It was inscribed

BERTHA HECK

Born Aug. 29, 1851

Died Jan. 31, 1927

Gone but not Forgotten

It seemed to mark the end of an era. I remembered that the *Hermanner Volksblatt,* yielding to the *Advertiser-Courier,* had discontinued publication in 1928.

St. George Cemetery, the Roman Catholic cemetery of Hermann, is on a high and rolling slope on the other outskirt of town, just off Goethe Street. It is a pleasant retreat, with a long *allée* overhung with spreading cedars, and it, too, is rich in sculptured sentiment, but the grave that caught and held my attention there was a new one. It was marked by a small bronze plaque, bright and shining in a glance of sunlight. The inscription read:

FLOYD H. ELSENRAAT

A1C U.S. Air Force

Vietnam

Dec. 24, 1949

Sept. 24, 1971

Hermann (perhaps because of its European roots) is plentifully provided with places to eat. I counted (and visited) eight of them. All were crowded at lunchtime, and two or three were filled at night. They are the A & W Drive-In, at the far south end of town; Imo's Pizza, across the Frene Creek bridge; the Sausage Shoppe (sandwiches and coffee); Schulte's Bakery (doughnuts and coffee); a bar-and-grill on First Street called Mr. R's; and three Market Street restaurants— Hillebrand's, the Central Hotel Café, and the Rockhouse. The Central Hotel Café keeps farmers' hours. It opens in the morning at six o'clock and closes at six in the evening. Hillebrand's and the Rockhouse keep hours more conveniently urban, and I ate most of my meals at one or the other of them. The food of Hermann includes some contributions from the traditional Missouri kitchen (country-cured ham, batter-fried chicken, catfish, cornbread, grits), but otherwise, except for the standard American fast food available at the A & W and at Imo's Pizza, it is wholly German. (A bumper sticker I often saw around town urged "Eat More Possum," but possum was never on any menu during my stay.) I dined at Hillebrand's on my first night in Hermann, and I ordered the evening special. It was a solid, and a satisfying, introduction to the local cuisine—sauerbraten with potato pancakes, apple sauce, and sauerkraut salad. My last meal in Hermann was a home-cooked dinner at the home of the Schweighausers. Mrs. Schweighauser (née Bezold) did the cooking, and the meal she gave us (in a house built in 1846 by her great-grandmother) was an even more satisfying valediction. The entrée was bratwurst with German potato salad. The vegetable was green beans cooked with bacon. There were side dishes of apple sauce and *Schmierkäse*. The bread was home-baked *Schnitzbrot.* The dessert was *Bundkuchen.* With the main course we drank a bottle of dry red wine from the Stone Hill Winery called Virginia Seedling.

I usually had my breakfast at the Rockhouse. It was just down the street from the German Haus—past a dark house in a deep lawn, with a broken bottle and a couple of beer cans under a forsythia bush (the only litter I ever saw anywhere in Hermann), past the Twin Trails liquor store, past Gosen's Gift Shop and Sporting Goods, past Jim's Barber Shop, past a Sears, Roebuck catalogue store, past Van Kamp's Boutique—with the sidewalk roofed or awninged almost all the way. The Rockhouse occupies the ground floors of two small adjoining buildings, the older of which (1842) is built of stone (a rarity in Hermann); hence its name. It is a comfortable place, with a low, beamed ceiling and a portion of the original two-foot-thick stone walls exposed, and the day's special chalked on a slate near the door (ham hock and beans, pot roast and dumplings, Wiener schnitzel), and it was nice to be able to look at the slate at breakfast and decide whether I wanted to come back that night for dinner. And the prices, too, were right. One night I finished dinner (spareribs) and was still hungry. I ordered a chocolate sundae. The waitress brought it, and added the charge to my bill. It was sixteen cents.

Dr. Schmidt, the optometrist, joined me for coffee at the Rockhouse one morning. "No," he said. "I don't mean that. Of course Hermann is a small town. And I hope it will stay that way. What I mean is, it isn't as small-town as it used to be. It's grown up a little bit. I remember when I first came here from Washington, Missouri, and before Mimi and I were married, I had a birthday, and Mimi baked me a cake. There was a woman down the street who used to let me practice on her piano in the evening, and when I went over that night, I took her a slice of my cake. She told me later what happened. She was working at the shoe factory then, and she packed her slice of cake in her lunchbox the next day. At lunchtime, she and her girl friend got to wondering who had baked the cake for me. My friend said maybe my mother, over in Washington. But the other woman said no. She said, 'I saw Doc when he got off the Washington bus yesterday, and he didn't have any packages with him.' "

There are three real-estate firms in Hermann. One of them, whose red-white-and-blue sign I often saw around town on vacant lots and empty buildings, is the Rathert Agency Realtors. It is owned and operated by Merlin T. Rathert and his wife, Judith. Rathert is a vigorous man of fifty-two. "Exactly, my friend," he told me. "We have a great heritage here, and it needs to be preserved. But with it we must be progressive. We can't be stymied by what is already here. I don't say tear down what we've got. I say maintain it, but plan for the future. I don't want big buildings. Anything over three or four stories is a no-no to me. What I'm saying, my friend, is we've got something here that a lot of communities would like to have. We must keep it, but we must also look ahead. People say don't change this quaint little town. I say grow, my friend. I say don't sit on your laurels."

A day or two later, I talked to Robert Kirchhofer, the president of the First Missouri Bank. Kirchhofer is thirty-five years old, and the youngest president in the history of the bank. "I don't know the answers," he told me. "I think I can say we want to stay small. We certainly don't want to see Hermann spread and sprawl. Take the shopping-center people. They turn up here from time to time, and they want to talk business. We always discourage them. The bank isn't interested in that kind of thing. But we have a very real problem here—a job problem. There are jobs to be had. There are offerings every week in the *Advertiser-Courier*. But they don't pay much more than unemployment compensation. It's the familiar small-town problem. How do you keep your young people? I was born and raised here. I love Hermann. I want it to stay Hermann. But I'm one of the lucky ones. I graduated from Hermann High School in 1959, and there were sixty of us in that class. I was one of five who went on to college, but only two of us came back to Hermann to stay. The other guy is a farmer. The three others couldn't find any college-graduate jobs here. There aren't even that many high-school-graduate jobs. And I say that ain't good."

Arlie Scharnhorst, the chairman of the board, joined Kirchhofer and me. It was he whom Kirchhofer succeeded as president of the bank. "I think we can survive," Scharnhorst told me. "I think we can keep the kind of Hermann we want. We've always had industry here—the shoe factory and one or two others. I hope we can solve the job problem without becoming really industrialized. And I hope we can avoid becoming a bedroom suburb for St. Louis. I think we can continue to stand on our own two feet. Our economy is sound. I don't know a farm in the area that's in any kind of trouble. Our people are savers. Always have been. There's a tradition here of thrift. That's one of our German virtues. These are ultra-conservative people. Especially when it comes to money. You may have heard what they say around here: 'Never bet on a sure thing unless you can afford to lose.'"

"One of the Poeschels built this house in 1869," Mrs. William Harrison told me. The Harrisons came to Hermann from Columbia, Missouri, the seat of the state university, and are one of the few non-German families in town. "He was a brother of the Poeschel who built the Stone Hill Winery, and he had some rather grand ideas. This is the only Greek Revival house in Hermann with columns of that size. We've had to completely restore it, of course. It was in the most dreadful shape when we bought it, in 1954. A moonshiner had it during Prohibition, and the people who lived here after that were too pitifully poor to keep from letting it run all the way down. We've tried to restore it to exactly what it was when Poeschel built it. The only real change we made, we added the fireplace in what we call the family room. Which brings up an interesting note. The Scharnhorsts, as you probably know, have the old Charles Eitzen house, which was built around 1850, and I'm sure you've noticed those beautiful white marble fireplaces. And Laura Graf, whose house was built in 1892, has that exquisite Victorian fireplace in her parlor. But our house belongs to a period somewhere in between. It was built at a time when the fireplace was considered old-fashioned, and the latest thing was the parlor stove."

The superintendent of schools in Hermann is a big, bald, sparkling, blue-eyed man named Ross Boeger. "I'm not a Hermannite," he told me. "I've only been here since 1973. But Hermann fits right into my background—I'm a native Missourian, and my ancestry is totally German. I admire these people. They're house-proud and they're self-disciplined and they're responsible. When we first moved here, I saw my neighbor out sweeping the street in front of his house, and I was amazed. But I soon found out that he was only doing what everybody does in Hermann. So now I do the same. Well, our pupils seem to have inherited that Old World respect for property. You won't find a mark of any kind on any wall in any rest room in any of our schools. No graffiti—none. And we don't have any locks on our lockers. We don't need them. Our people don't steal. Another thing is, the parents here believe that the school is authority, and they give the school the right to teach *and* to discipline. And this is on top of some very strict home discipline. We do a real job of teaching here, too. Our grading is rigid. I have two children who were still in school when we came to Hermann. They'd always been better-than-average students, but when they started in here they had to work harder than ever before in their lives. I'll tell you something that bugs me. We're told that the young people now can't read or do math as well as the youngsters did thirty or forty years ago. Well, I don't believe it. The difference is this: In the old days, a whole lot of young people dropped out of school very early. They were the poor students, mostly. But now they stay in school, and they naturally pull the average down. I'm really enthusiastic about this town. Did I tell you we start teaching German here in the third grade? It's not a real course at that level. It's just offered, like passing around a box of candy. The German teacher comes into the class one day a week or so, and she starts by saying something like '*Guten Tag.*' Then she tells the kids what it means, and writes the words on the board. The next week, she starts them on '*ein, zwei, drei.*' The kids can pay attention or not. But German is a real course in high school, with an average enrollment in German 1 of around thirty. Now let's move into the shadows. We have our problems here. We have the rumor of drugs. If I were to ask one of our youngsters could he get his hands on some pot this afternoon, the answer would probably be yes. If you ask me is there any in the school, the answer is no. We had a marijuana dog up here a while ago. He was paraded through the halls and past the lockers. Nothing. But by four o'clock this afternoon there'll be a lot of our young people sitting somewhere and smoking their pot. I think we have a little drinking problem, too. But not in the school—not in this building or on any school grounds. School is for schooling."

The *Advertiser-Courier* had had a story, with pictures, headed "TOP RANKING HHS SENIORS." There were thirteen of them—twelve girls and one boy. In the hall outside Boeger's office, I recognized one of the girls. She was Mary Jo Pohlman, a pretty girl with long blond hair and a wide, confident smile. She ranked tenth in the group of thirteen, just ahead of the one boy. "Oh, I'm a feminist," she told me. "I really believe in liberation. I want a career. I'm going to study nursing. But I want to marry, too. The only thing is, I guess

I'm also a little old-fashioned. I mean, I like those opened doors."
"Those what?" I said.
"You know," she said. "I like a guy to open the door for me."

I met the Reverend Mr. Klemme, pastor of the United Church of Christ, by appointment, in his office overlooking the river. He is a tall, gray man, with an air of troubled severity. He sat with his back to the view. "I like small towns," he told me. "I feel they represent the best of America. I particularly like Hermann. I'm only sorry that the morals of the city are beginning to reach us here. We had eight pregnancies among our high-school girls last year. But I attribute that to more than moral laxity. By that I mean the problem is complex. Our economy here is very importantly to blame. There seems to be plenty of work, but the wages in all of the ordinary jobs are low. They are often so low that both husband and wife must go out to work. Moral laxity is a direct result of a lack of parental control. There is nobody at home when the children come home from school. And in the evening the parents are both too tired and don't want to be bothered. Our confirmation classes used to be obligatory. Now the parents consult the children. The *parents* consult the *children!*"

The Scharnhorsts are members of the United Church, and Mrs. Scharnhorst (née Heck) is an active volunteer there. She seemed to share some of the Reverend Mr. Klemme's concerns. "Abortion is unheard-of here," she told me. "It isn't even discussed. So the poor girls just go ahead and have their illegitimate babies. And they're only children themselves—fifteen or sixteen years old. Even fourteen! Half the time, they don't even know who the father is. But the strange thing—the thing that is so hard for my generation to understand—is this: It's no disgrace. They're not ostracized. Nobody even seems to mind. Not even when the baby turns out to be half black. Or half white. Or whatever. What worries me is when the father isn't known. Some of those babies are going to grow up and maybe marry their half brother or half sister. And never even know it."

It is generally agreed, though often deplored, that Hermann is a growing town. For all its isolation, its limited economy, the drift away of its young people, its population increases every year. Most of the newcomers are city people—fugitives, for the most part, from St. Louis. Most of them also seem to have arrived by chance and to have settled down on impulse. "It's really almost eerie," Mrs. Bessie Moore, my landlady at the German Haus, told me one afternoon over coffee and a slice of crumb cake still warm from the oven. "People come through here, and something seems to happen, and they decide to stay. I can't explain it. Van and I were born and raised in St. Louis, and we had a successful printing business. I suppose we were getting a little restless. I suppose it's those big-city blues. Anyway, we were out driving through the country one weekend, and we turned off the Interstate at New Florence and wandered along and came over the bridge, and there we were in Hermann. I don't think I'd ever even heard of Hermann. But halfway down Market Street I had this feeling. It felt like an electric charge. I said to Van, 'Here it is—I've finally made it home!' I said, 'Nothing but good can happen to us here.' "

"I'd call it an accident," Ken Boyer, the former Cardinals star, told me. "I sure didn't plan it that way. Porter Tumy, who has that big farm across the river, brought me down to Hermann in the fall of 1961 for some quail shooting, and I liked it here. I thought it was a real fine place. I still do. It has something. I mean besides the shooting. Because there isn't a whole lot of quail shooting left. Too much cow and plow."

The newest newcomers to Hermann whom I got to know were a couple named Tucker—Frank and Phyllis Tucker. Both are in their forties. Tucker is a teacher by profession. Before coming to Hermann, he taught for fifteen years in a suburban St. Louis high school. He works now as a housepainter and paperhanger. His wife is an artist. "We've been here just over a year," she told me. "We had made up our minds to leave St. Louis, and we had heard about this farm near Gerald, down in Franklin County, and we got on the wrong road and ended up here in Hermann. We'd been here before, for a Maifest, and the only impression we had of Hermann was a lot of people rushing around. But this was a beautiful spring day. We really saw the town. And we decided we'd like to see more, so we checked into the German Haus. Then we went out to look around. We came down Third Street and saw this house with Merlin Rathert's sign out front, and we liked everything about it—the lovely block, the lovely pink brick, and the way it's built close to the street, so there's plenty of room in back for a big garden. Frank said, 'Let's not think about it—let's just do it.' So we bought it. I don't know exactly when it was built, but we have a copy of the original abstract for the land. It was a federal grant to a man named Hensley in 1832, and Mr. Bayer, the Gesellschaft agent, bought it from Hensley in 1837. That kind of continuity pleases me. We bought the house from the estate of an old man named Henry Bohl. Mr. Bohl died a few years ago from a stomach obstruction. The obstruction turned out to be a mass of wood splinters. Mr. Bohl was one of those men who are always chewing on a toothpick. There's a story that he had thirty thousand dollars in cash hidden somewhere in this house. We keep hoping, but we haven't found it yet."

"We could use it," Tucker said. "But the important thing is just being here in this wonderful, friendly town. Phyllis didn't mention why we wanted to leave St. Louis. The high school where I taught was a joy when I first started there. Then something began to change. The community began to go down. We began to get a whole new kind of student. Nobody seemed to want to learn. I'd look at those sullen, resentful faces. It got so I was spending half of every hour on discipline. We had security guards patrolling the halls. And this was a community that had once been the flower of St. Louis County. I went on teaching the way I'd always taught, and when the first set of grades came out last year, there was an uproar. I had failed fifty-two per cent of my classes. The uproar came from the students. The principal just sat in his office, trying to hang on till retirement. My classes were impossible. There was always some kid jumping up and threatening he was going to get me. I never actually had a knife pulled on me, but the knives were there. I'll tell you something. If you've never had a girl stand up in class and cuss you out in language so vile you've hardly even heard a man use it—well, if you haven't had that experience, you can't imagine what it does to your insides. I'd go home at night and I wouldn't know whether to cry or get drunk. I decided I didn't have to stay there anymore. And nobody asked me to stay. None of the administrators cared. They thought I was crazy. Quality education isn't the point anymore. The point is fill a slot and keep order. I'm not worried about making a living. I might try teaching again, here in Hermann. It's a whole different system. But I've always been handy with my hands. And I'm beginning to get a reputation for good, honest workmanship. I feel I've saved my soul."

"There's something *Frank* didn't mention," Mrs. Tucker said. "He's probably the only paperhanger or housepainter in Gasconade County with a master's degree in education."

# The Grower's Shadow

It is four o'clock on a warm spring afternoon, and I am sitting at the counter of the Mobil Cafe in the crossroads hamlet of Wilder, Idaho, in the Canyon County flats of the Snake River Valley, some thirty miles west of Boise. I am sitting with the chief Canyon County agent. He is a big, easy, weathered man of fifty-four named Merle R. Samson, and we have stopped here for a cup of coffee after a day in an air-conditioned pickup truck, poking around a dusty countryside of farms and orchards and distant mountains. The Cafe is full of farmers in bib overalls and pointed boots. Samson is known to many of them, and they nod and call him by name. Most of the farmers are white, but two are Japanese and one is a dark-skinned Mexican. They are drinking the watery café coffee and talking in voices that would carry across a feedlot.

". . . malathion."

"Yes, sir. I mean No. 1 Idaho bakers."

"No, by God. What it turned out to be was the *web*worm."

"That's right. Sixty cents a hundredweight to the grower."

"You want to know what I think of malathion? I'd sooner *pee* on my alfalfa."

"Well, two days later he was down at Salt Lake City, and he walked into the Safeway store, and son of a bitch—they were selling the same potatoes there at the equivalent of thirteen dollars a hundredweight."

"And now the bastards say I can't use dieldrin. I say we ought to dump some dieldrin on the goddam ecologists."

"It's all those sons of bitches in between. They got their hand in *everybody's* pocket."

A county agent is the representative, at the barnyard level, of the Coöperative (state and federal) Agricultural Extension Service. It is he who brings to the farmer the fully ripened fruits of agronomical research. The county served by Samson and four other agents—an entomologist and three specialists in crops and cattle—plus two home economists, is an exemplar of that service. Canyon is the leading agricultural county in Idaho, and, with an annual farm income of more than seventy-eight million dollars, derived from a cornucopia of crops—sugar beets, apples, sweet-corn seed, hops, potatoes, alfalfa seed, cattle, peppermint, red-clover seed, wheat, onions, lima-bean seed, cherries, milk, prunes, barley, alfalfa hay, spinach, peaches, popcorn—it is one of the most productive counties in the nation. That was why I was there.

The office of the Canyon County agent is in Caldwell (pop. 14,219), the Canyon County seat. It is situated on the lumberyard-and-warehouse side of the Union Pacific tracks, and occupies a nest of low-ceilinged rooms on the second floor of a two-story stucco building that was once a garage. The ground floor houses the A-Gem Supply Company. A long flight of steps at one end of the building leads steeply up to a labyrinthine corridor lined with open doors and racks of United States Department of Agriculture publications: "Controlling the Mexican Bean Beetle," "Diseases of Mint," "A Career for Me in Agriculture," "Growing Carrot Seed in Idaho." I had climbed those steps for the first time at around nine o'clock that morning. Samson's room was the first open door on the left. He was there, at his desk, talking on the telephone. He looked up and smiled and pointed to a chair. I removed a pile of papers and an apple—a big red, shiny Delicious apple—to the top of a filing cabinet and sat down. Through the window there was a view of a warehouse roof, and above the roof was an immensity of sky—the wide blue sky of the mountain West.

"And how about the leaves?" Samson was saying on the telephone.
"Right. It looks a lot like wild parsley. Or wild carrot. And the root
is very often mistaken for wild parsnip. . . . Well, that's what it
sounds like to me. I think you've got yourself some poison hemlock
there. . . . No, you sure don't. . . . You bet it is—it's very toxic.
What I think you better do is fence that area off and treat it with
a chemical weed killer, like maybe 2,4-D. . . . Right. And the sooner
the better."

Samson hung up and swung around in his chair. His face was
lined and deeply tanned. "Well," he said, and lighted a cigarette.
"I'll tell you the truth. That's the only thing I don't much like about
this job. I mean the telephone. I'm a county agent that likes to be
out in the county. But I guess it could be worse. I know it could. I
quit the Service back in 1951 and tried it out in the world. I went
into the feed-and-grain business. I stayed out there for three years,
and that was enough. I was more than ready to come back. County
agents don't often get rich, but they get a lot of real job satisfaction—
they're giving instead of taking. And they don't have to sit at a
desk all day. At least, not every day."

The telephone rang. Samson swung back to his desk. He answered
and listened and brightened. "Right," he said. "You bet I do—I
was down there a couple of days ago. But it depends on what you
want. You've got a good location there. The conditions are very good.
If you want to try a legume, I'll have to suggest alfalfa. You might
try mixing alfalfa and orchard grass. . . . You bet. It makes a real
fine permanent pasture. . . . Oh, I don't know—I guess forty-sixty
would be about the best proportion. Or you could try just a sprinkling
of alfalfa and the rest grass. Or all grass. . . . Right. And, of course,
grass is a good soil builder. But if you're going to broadcast it, I'd
increase that just a little—maybe ten pounds to the acre. . . . Well,
sure. And with an all-grass pasture you don't have to worry about
bloat in your cows. . . . You bet."

Samson hung up. He sat for a moment, rubbing his left ear. "I
guess I've been pretty lucky," he said. "I know what I want, and
I've got it. I was born and raised in Idaho, and, except for the Navy
Air Corps in the Second World War, I've never had to leave it. I
got my B.S. at the University, up at Moscow. I've worked up there,
in Latah County, and I've worked in the east, around Pocatello.

I've been all over the state. And Canyon County here is the best of Idaho. They call this Treasure Valley. We've got a diversity of crops which I doubt can be matched anywhere. That makes it interesting. I like a little variety. But we've got some specialties, too. We're the No. 1 county in the country—in the whole United States—in sweet-corn-seed production. And in alfalfa seed. And red-clover seed. And mixed grains. We're No. 5 in sugar beets. We're way up in dairy production. And so on. We've never had a crop failure. There's been some reduced yields here, but never an out-and-out failure. And it all began from nothing. Sixty years ago, this county was a wasteland. It was nothing but sagebrush desert. We get only about eight inches of rain a year. It was irrigation that made the difference, of course. We have plenty of underground water here, but we don't irrigate with that. We don't mine our underground reserves, the way some states are doing. The water we use is mountain snow-melt, impounded in storage lakes."

The telephone rang. Samson turned and looked at it. But he answered it on the third ring. "Oh," he said. "How you doing? . . . Right. . . . Yes, so I understand. . . . That's right. . . . Well, you've sprayed enough acreage to know. . . . You bet." He laughed. "But just remember, Roy. Remember what Hugh Homan told you about malathion and the paint on automobiles. It acts like a solvent."

Samson hung up. "That's enough," he said. He stood up. "Let's get out of here. Let's go see how the season is going. I'll take you for a little drive."

Hugh Homan is the entomologist assigned to Canyon County. I met him the following morning—a thickset man of thirty-eight with a hard blue jaw and heavy black brows and sideburns. He invited me to join him on a round of professional calls. We drove out of town on a wide gravel road in a dirty white Volkswagen with a big can of Treflan weed killer bouncing around in back. The sky overhead was fresh and blue, but there were cloudy mountains on the horizon. Homan's right hand, on the wheel, was missing the thumb and forefinger. "This fellow I want to see first is a fruitgrower named Norman Vermeer," he said. "He's got a problem with sandburs in one of his orchards. I should have seen him yesterday, but I had to go over to Boise and testify in an accident case. A farmer was burning a crop residue, and the smoke blew across the road, and a driver came along and couldn't see, and stopped. Another car came up and didn't see him sitting there, and smashed into him. Killed him. So his family is suing the farmer for negligence. I testified on farming practices. Burning crop residue instead of tilling it back into the soil is bad farming. But I had to testify that they do it all the time. It's common practice. Farming is a hazardous occupation, and one big reason is carelessness. I grew up on a farm just north of here, in Payette County, and I learned my lesson early. I was just sixteen when I lost my fingers. I was running a balky old corn picker, and I tried to reach under the rollers to fix something without turning off the engine. The only lucky thing was, I happened to be left-handed."

We slowed to turn off onto a bumpy lane, and my window filled with a sudden sugary jasmine smell of wild currant. There was a fence-line thicket of blossoming bushes just across the road. A yellow-headed blackbird was perched on one of the flowering branches.

"Now, there's a pretty sight," Homan said.

"The blackbird?" I said.

"What?" he said. "Oh—heck, no. I mean that old rooster pheasant marching across that field. I've got a date with him for next fall. This is real good country here. I mean for farming *and* living. We start off in September with a season on doves. Then sage grouse. Then quail: bobwhite and mountain and valley—all three. Then pheasant. Then, up in the hills, chukar and Hungarian partridge. That's good, hard hunting. Then ducks and geese down along the river. Then, later on, if you've got the ambition to pack into the mountains, there's elk. I reload my own shotgun shells, and last fall I used a hundred pounds of lead, in one-and-a-quarter-ounce shot. So you can see I did a little bit of shooting. But I don't have any trouble enjoying my weekends any time of the year. We've got trout fishing in the spring, and there's bass and perch in the lakes in summer. And there's good skiing up in the mountains. This isn't just the place where I was born and raised. This country here is my *home.*"

We pulled into a rutted driveway between a big storage barn and a little white house in a sombre grove of pines. Beyond the drive were the pink-canopied aisles of a peach orchard. A tall, blond smiling young man came out through the pines to meet us. He was Vermeer.

"Hugh," he said. "This sandbur situation here is serious. Those little farmers are mean. They made trouble for me with my pickers last fall. You know those fishhook barbs—they'll dig right through your pants. My pickers couldn't stand it. And you know about good pickers."

"I know they're hard to get," Homan said. "But maybe I can help. Anyway, I brought you this can of Treflan. I want you to try it. One quart to the acre in forty gallons of water. Then we'll see. Where are they giving you trouble—in your peach orchard there?"

"They're in my plums. You want to take a look?"

"You bet. Your peaches look good, Norman. Did you light for that frost back there?"

"I probably should have. I took a chance. And for once I was lucky. I understand they're hurting bad on stone fruits up in Washington."

"So I hear."

Vermeer laughed. "Well, you know how we feel about that. We sit down every night and pray that Washington freezes out. Then we might have a chance to make some money."

"Hey," Homan said. "You really do have some sandburs here."

"They're healthy little farmers," Vermeer said. "And these plums are one of my best crops. They all go back to New York—they're all for the kosher market."

"That's a good contract market."

"It is—but, you know, I wonder about those people back there. They buy all the plums I can grow, but they've never tasted a real plum. I mean a ripe plum. To get them there in the condition the market wants, I've got to pick them three weeks early. But they're really good plums when they ripen on the tree. The pickers always leave a few on every tree for us."

"The consumer is the boss."

"That's the trouble. The consumer eats with her eyes. It's funny, isn't it? She won't buy an apple unless it looks like a picture. It has to be big and red and shiny. But you and I and every grower knows that a little green adds flavor, and the redder the skin the tougher it is. I doubt if I'd even grow a red Delicious if she didn't make me. I might grow Jonathans or Rome Beauties. This is the best Rome country in the world."

"She'll change her mind someday," Homan said. "The fashion will turn to something else. Remember the Baldwin and the McIntosh and the old Arkansas Black."

"I know she'll change," Vermeer said. "And then I'll have to pull out half of my orchard."

We followed a long flat, empty blacktop road. Flanking it were boundless potato fields. Then the land began to dip. We passed a hopyard, with its twenty-foot poles and overhead wires and clustering, climbing vines. We came around the slope of a crumbling, sunbaked butte. We passed a barn remodelled into a house, and then a leafy alfalfa field. We turned into a drive at a gray shingle house with a straggle of sheds and shacks in back. There was a sound of hammering from behind the sheds.

Homan shut off the engine and leaned on the wheel. "This is a highly successful alfalfa-seed operation," he said. "It's a partnership. A couple named Trueblood live in that barn over there, and an old batch named Wally Burrill lives here. Bud Trueblood grows the alfalfa, and Wally raises the bees. Alfalfa is pollinated by a species of leaf-cutter bee. Those sheds with the open fronts are mobile bee boxes. Domesticated leaf-cutter bees don't live in hives. They nest in the holes of perforated boards called bee boards. The average board will have around two thousand holes, and there are usually twelve cells— twelve bees—to the hole. The bees are kept in refrigerated hibernation until just before blossomtime. Then the boards are hung in the sheds and hauled out to the field. Alfalfa pollination requires a lot of bees— between seven and ten thousand to the acre. And only the females work. This kind of beekeeping is full of problems. But that isn't why I'm here. There isn't much that I can teach Wally and Bud about their business. They're exceptional. What usually happens, I learn from them. So I like to stop by whenever I'm around this part of the country. And Mary Trueblood is a real good cook."

The hammering stopped, and a gray-haired man with a bony face and rimless glasses appeared. "I heard you drive in," he said, "but I was up on the roof of a shed. I've finally built me some sheds I like."

"I was looking at that new one over there," Homan said. "How come you're using planks?"

"Oh, Jesus," Burrill said. "I got sick of that goddam plywood. It's so goddam phony. But that isn't the only difference. These new sheds have all got double roofs for good ventilation. I want to make those little bastards comfortable. And I'm hinging the bottom planks on all three walls for the same reason. They're just as sensitive to heat as they are to cold."

"A lot of growers don't seem to realize that," Homan said. "They have to learn the hard way."

"You're goddam right," Burrill said. "A bee don't come alive until the temperature gets to seventy plus, and he'll die at one hundred and five. You've got to watch the little bastards. I remember one morning a couple of years ago I was making a round of my sheds. The early sun was shining in the open fronts, and the temperature up at board level—about chest level—was seventy-one degrees, and the bees were dropping out of their holes. But the floor in the sheds was still cold, and they lay there turning numb. What I did was grab a broom and race around sweeping them out—sweeping them out into the sun. And son of a bitch—it only took a minute of sunshine. Then they sat up and flew off to start making me some money. I could have lost every goddam bee I had."

"A lot of people have," Homan said.

Homan and I had noon dinner with the Truebloods and Wally Burrill in Mary Trueblood's kitchen. The Truebloods are in their fifties. She is a pretty woman with soft gray hair, and he is tall and lanky and burned to leather. We sat in comfortable chairs at a long table with a centerpiece of red tulips. We began with roast lamb, baked potatoes, and fresh green asparagus, and finished with cherry pie and coffee. The asparagus had been cut (by Mrs. Trueblood) only that morning from a volunteer stand along a fencerow. In Canyon County, asparagus is a weed. The seeds are spread by birds, and the plants thrive wherever they can escape cultivation—in the shelter of fences and around the trunks of orchard trees.

"I remember when we took out our orchard up home," Homan said. "My job was to dig up the asparagus roots around the trees. Those roots were harder to get out than the stumps."

"I've broken a plow on asparagus roots," Trueblood said. "I detest it with a purple passion. Except when it's here on my plate."

The stove on which the asparagus, and everything else, was cooked was a coal stove—a big black cast-iron turn-of-the-century Majestic range.

"I spent years finding that stove," Mrs. Trueblood said. "I wouldn't cook on anything else. Coal heat is the perfect cooking heat. Of course, it's more trouble than gas or electricity, but that's true of so *many* things. So many good things take trouble. Like this homemade bread we're eating. And homemade pie. And homegrown vegetables. I love my Majestic stove. And one day when I was up in Bud's mother's attic I found another treasure. It's hanging there over the stove: 'The Majestic Cook Book.' "

"Hell's bells," Burrill said. "Everything worthwhile takes trouble."

"I had to learn that for myself," Trueblood said. "I had to go all the way to college to find out how to farm. My father sure never taught me. He farmed on the principle of let's hurry up and make as much as we can right now and never mind what happens to the soil. It never occurred to him to give nature half a chance. But the things I finally learned weren't new. A year or two ago, I picked up a copy of the Department of Agriculture *Yearbook* for 1902— and it's all in there. Crop rotation. Soil conservation. Cultivation. The Extension Service tried to teach it to my dad, but he couldn't be bothered. He couldn't even be bothered to irrigate right. It was easier to overwater, so he leached his soil away."

"There are still a lot of farmers like your dad," Homan said. "We've worked out a little table at the office. We figure that maybe two per cent of the farmers are truly receptive to new ideas. They're men like you and Wally. We call them innovators. Then comes a group of fifteen per cent that we call early adapters. Then comes a middle group of sixty per cent. They're the regular majority. They come in when the ideas are pretty well established. Another fifteen per cent are the late adapters. They're the ones that say, 'Hell, I'm doing all right, these new ideas are probably just a flash in the pan, so I guess I'll wait and see.' And then there's those that never adapt."

"We got one of those bastards for a neighbor," Burrill said. "He told me he wouldn't think of using fertilizer. He said it made the weeds grow too fast."

"A lot of farmers come to our meetings just to get away from their wives," Homan said. "Or maybe to see their friends. They don't even try to learn."

"Learning is hard work," Trueblood said. "But, good Lord, so is chukar hunting."

The Snake River swings up from the south a mile or two west of the Trueblood farm, and Homan and I crossed it there on the Homedale Bridge. The river was fast and muddy, with many brushy islands, and the banks were lined with drooping willows. On the other side of the river, beyond the one-street village of Homedale, the road began to rise. Our destination was a hilltop orchard owned by a man named Shults. "Garfield Shults," Homan said. "He called me out here a couple of weeks ago for advice on spraying his apple trees for scale. I want to see how good a job he did. Garfield sells all his fruit at retail. He's an old-fashioned door-to-door peddler, and he makes enough to live the way he wants to. His real interest is grafting—experimenting with different species and varieties. I met a man from Cornell at the annual meeting of the Entomological Society of America last year. 'So you're from Idaho,' he said. 'I wonder if you know a man named Garfield Shults. He just wrote and asked me for some New York McIntosh slips.' Garfield's known from coast to coast."

Shults's orchard was a jungle. Towering, tortured, unpruned apple trees. Bushy pears and peaches and plums. Reedlike saplings half buried in thigh-high grass. We found Shults down on his knees hacking at the roots of an apricot stump. He stood up to greet us—a small, ragged, beaming man in a khaki sun helmet. "Hugh," he said. "You know something? I think that spray did good."

"I think so, too," Homan said. "All the scale I've seen is dead." He rubbed his hand along an apple branch. "Nothing left but dust."

"And that tree there was just about lathered with them."

"That's right. But, my God, Garfield—when are you going to mow this grass? This is no way to grow fruit."

"Oh, I'm going to mow it. Don't worry about that. But right now I've got something to show you. Here's a row that's really dizzy. I've got prune plums growing on an apricot tree. The way I figure— if the prunes freeze out, I've still got a crop of apricots."

"Right."

"This whole section is dizzy. This dizzy-looking tree is my experimental laboratory. I've got it growing seven or eight different apples—

Roanoke from Virginia, McIntosh from New York, Splendor from New Zealand, and Spies and Jonathans and Romes. And I've got a mystery apple here. I crossed a red and a golden Delicious. It's got those wide Delicious shoulders. But it's pink, Hugh—it's just as pink as a peach blossom. Oh, and here's a berserk Bartlett pear. Now, what the heck did I do here? I've forgotten, except that it keeps as good as a Bosc. And here's another berserk tree where I've forgotten exactly what I did. But I'll be watching it. I'll find out in a couple of months. That's half the fun. Is it going to be something delectable? Or merely edible? Or do you feed it to the horses? But I wanted to ask you, Hugh. What am I going to do about those bugs?"

"I keep telling you, Garfield. We can't get rid of bugs. We can't *eradicate* them. We don't even want to. They've got their place."

"O.K. But what do I *do?*"

"You learn to live with them, Garfield."

Homan and I climbed back up through the overgrown aisles in a susurration of bees. We came out of the orchard dusk and into the hilltop afternoon. "Garfield is like so many farmers," Homan said. "They're chemical activists. We're trying hard to change all that. We're trying to teach them that insecticides are the last resort. They mean you've failed at proper control—biological control. Our target orchard insect is the codling moth. It puts the worm in the apple. But when we first learned how to kill the codling moth chemically, we also killed the predators of the spider mite, and the spider mite became a very serious problem. Then we started using less toxic stuff on the codling moth and spared the predators. Now we're working to control the codling moth by confusing him at breeding time with a synthetic female scent. I think the farmers are beginning to listen to us. Not because they're fascinated by the idea of biological control. They listen because they're businessmen, and insecticides cost money. They cost a lot of money."

The senior home economist in the Canyon County office is a tall, fair, blue-eyed woman of thirty named Beverly Montgomery. Mrs. Montgomery and I had a cup of coffee together in her office. It is a windowless room with a desk, a filing cabinet, and a big 4-H poster: "I pledge my Head to clearer thinking, my Heart to greater loyalty, my Hands to larger service, and my Health to better living, for my

Club, my Community, and my Country." "My work is mostly with our nutrition-education program," she said. "This is a rich county in many ways, but we have a lot of low-income families—welfare and food-stamp people. We have poor white people and poor Mexicans. Our Japanese families all seem to be self-sufficient. I would say that at least one-third of our population needs nutritional guidance. It's distressing how poorly informed they are, and how improvident. At the first of the month, when they have some money, they eat well. I mean, by their standards—hamburger, hot dogs, potato chips, Cokes, and the snack foods they see advertised on television. Television is a problem. It's the only source of information that these people have. They don't read newspapers or magazines, and few of them have had much schooling. Television commercials are their guides to living. Well, they tend to blow their budget in the first two weeks of the month. The third week is pretty tight. And by the fourth week they are often quite literally down to plain rice or macaroni. With no sauce, no butter—nothing. Then they get their checks or stamps, and they're so hungry for good food they'll blow it again on impulse—on strawberries at seventy-nine cents a pound, or half a dozen avocados at forty cents apiece. And this is where television comes into it again. They will spend their food money for something like Geritol. Our work is to help them stretch their food dollar—to help them get the most and the best for their money. It isn't easy work. We can't work directly with these people. We represent something they don't understand. They're suspicious and resentful. We have to reach them through their own kind of people. I have five white and three Mexican aides. These are superior women I have been able to attract and interest in our program—women I have trained. They are often neighbors of the people we wish to help. They can go into those homes and talk to the women there—the poor, unhappy teenage wives who send their kids to school without breakfast. They're down on life. Everything is too much for them. They've given up. But my aides are dedicated and patient. They go in and show them how to plan. They show them how to buy. They show them how hot cereal is cheaper and more nutritious than the cold cereals they hear about on television. They teach them how to cope."

We were driving out through a misty morning countryside—John Henry, who is the Canyon County livestock specialist, and I—in an old Mercury sedan with a mobile weighing chute clanking along behind, to weigh some calves at the farm of a breeder of purebred Red Angus cattle. Henry is forty-one years old—a big, bald, round-faced, slouching man—and he was dressed in the uniform of the stockman: olive-green coveralls and pointed boots. "You know what they say about getting a farm these days," he said. "There's only two ways. Either you inherit it or you marry into it. This old fellow we're going to see, this Layton Todd, he founded the operation, but he and his son are running it together now. What we're going to do this morning is weigh some calves for registry with the Red Angus Association. These calves are all around two hundred days old, and if they're up to standard they should weigh around five hundred pounds. I like working with cattle, but I guess I prefer it this way. My wife and I both like living in town—she plays the organ at the Latter-Day Saints. I grew up on a stock farm. My dad had one of the first Black Angus herds in Idaho. Red Angus is something new. I started milking at the age of six, and at eight I was out there shovelling manure, and when I was old enough for 4-H work I started feeding steers. I saw a lot. I saw my dad knocked down three times and almost killed one day by a dairy bull. Dairy bulls are always inclined to be mean. I got knocked around and cut up pretty good quite a few times myself. And I saw one of my kid friends out baling hay one day, and he slipped and went into the baler. It wired him up like a bale of hay, and the plunger cut him in two. I left the farm when I left home for college. Besides, my dad is still working our place. I got my B.S. in animal husbandry and my M.S. in animal nutrition. This work is exactly right for me. I like to teach. I like to be of service, to make some impact. And everybody knows you. You're a leading citizen." He laughed. "I mean—Well, gosh, I get my picture in the paper at least once a month."

A sign appeared just ahead on the left: "Black Dust Angus Farms." Henry turned off the road, and we clanked down a lane past a block of cattle corrals tumultuous with bellowing cows and moaning calves. There was a heavy smell of manure and the sour and sickening stink of ensilage. We pulled up at a loading chute halfway down the block.

Layton Todd, a red-faced man in coveralls and a big straw hat, was leaning against the chute. Inside the chute, tinkering with a gate, was a pink-cheeked younger man. That was his son, Ze Todd. ("People are always asking me about my name," he later told me. "They ought to ask my dad and mother. They saw this movie about Jesse James just before I was born, and Jesse's wife, her name was Zee. My dad and mother had pretty well decided that I was going to be a girl, and that name of Zee appealed to them. And when I turned out to be a boy, they dropped an 'e' and gave it to me anyway.") Henry got out and unhitched the weighing chute, and Layton Todd came over and gave him a hand. It was a narrow barred cage on wheels, with a drop gate at one end. Henry and Layton hauled it up alongside one of the corrals. Ze pushed his corral gate open and swung it back to form a pen between the corral and the chute.

"I got three calves here, John," Layton said. "The only trouble is, there's one that's a little too old and two a little too young. Can we adjust? I'd hate to have you turn right around and drive on back to town."

"No problem," Henry said. "A few days don't make all that much difference."

"They're big, too. I tell you, John—these Red Angus calves, they grow faster than the Black. They got that hybrid vigor. All right, Ze. Let's start with that little bull."

A howling, balking, slobbering calf came stumbling through the loading chute. Ze Todd trotted in behind it, swinging a ski pole cut off short for a goad. He prodded it across the makeshift pen and up to the weighing chute. The gate was up, and Henry stood ready to drop it closed. I leaned up over the fence to watch. The calf shied and lurched—and skittered into the fence. The impact bounced me off and sat me down hard on the ground. I heard Henry shout, and Layton call, "Turn him, Ze! He's got himself bass-ackwards." The calf gave a long, despairing cry. Layton now had a rope around its neck, and, with Ze prodding and Henry waving it on, it dodged, bawling and blubbering, over the threshold and into the chute. The gate dropped with a crash. The little bull stood heaving on the scales. The cows and calves in the corrals all raised their heads and bellowed.

The two other calves were heifers. One was about the size of the little bull and the other was somewhat larger, but they both went almost readily into the weighing chute. The bull was the youngest (one hundred and eighty-seven days) and the lightest (three hundred and forty-five pounds). The larger, and older, of the heifer calves weighed four hundred and ninety-four pounds. It was the last to be weighed. It lumbered back into the corral, back through the staring cows and calves, back to its bellowing mother—drooling, wide-eyed, whimpering

We stood and watched it go.

"The fuss they make," Henry said. "They act like they think they're beef. If they only knew how lucky they are. They've got the easy life. Nothing to do but breed."

"They got it easier than the breeder," Layton said.

"Dad's right," Ze said. "Breeding cattle isn't like raising, say, chickens. A full-grown purebred bull is a lot of animal. He can service six or seven cows in a day, and it's easy enough to get him started. The trouble is, those cows all look alike to him. So the problem is to get him to service them all—to move him on from No. 1 to No. 2 and from her to No. 3. All you've got is that ring in his nose. It isn't only that bulls can be mean. They're big—they can weigh a ton. I mean, two *thousand* pounds. An animal that big can give you just a little nudge and you'll feel it for a couple of weeks."

"It's like getting nudged by a truck," Henry said.

Samson said, "Which field is it, George?"

George—George Shavers—turned and spat out a wad of tobacco, and lighted a cigarette. "It's both," he said. "But this eighteen acres here is probably the worst. I've only had it just three years, and I've done everything I could, but it don't seem to do no good. I don't know, Merle. The guy that had it before me, he must have let it run down for twenty years."

"I'll bet he did," Samson said. "Well, let's go take a look. You want to take my truck or yours?"

"Mine," Shavers said. "Yours looks too nice and new for these old fields. You know, on top of everything else, I think I've got some gophers coming in. I found a couple of holes the other day. But I wonder what they're going to find to eat in that damn field."

Shavers climbed under the wheel of an old Ford pickup, and Samson and I squeezed in beside him. Samson sat with his tools in his lap—a foot-long tubular soil probe, like a giant apple corer, and a dozen paper soil-sample bags marked "University of Idaho Agricultural Extension Service Soil Testing Laboratory Take Soil Samples Carefully Take a Representative Sample Use Separate Bag for Each Sample." We moved off across the field, jolting against the grain of the furrows.

"There was a young guy down at the café," Shavers said. "He told me manure didn't do no good. I think it was just a theory he had. So I didn't pay no attention."

"I don't know who that young guy was," Samson said. "But he sure wasn't any farmer. The only possible drawback to manure is that it might bring you in some foreign weeds. But I don't call that much of a drawback."

"It ain't to me," Shavers said. "I've already got every damn weed there is."

"O.K., George. Let's pull up here."

We got out in a following cloudburst of dust. It passed, and the air cleared, and I could see the sudden rise of the mountains, twenty miles away. Samson squatted down and worked his probe into the soil as far as it would go. He extracted a core of crumbly earth. He sifted it through his fingers and into a sample bag.

"Sandy loam," he said. "But you've got some clay down deep. I don't like that much. Suppose we move on down the line a couple of hundred yards and try again. Maybe this isn't typical. And, of course, the laboratory may have something else to say."

"I like a sandy loam," Shavers said.

"I do, too," Samson said. "If you water it enough. And often enough. And you need organic matter. I do think you're going to need a lot of manure for this field. Twenty tons to the acre, at least. But I like the tilth. I can see you've worked at cultivation. I don't see all those weeds you were talking about."

"It's cultivation, all right," Shavers said. "It ain't weed killer. I think weed killer is the lazy man's way."

"It's one of his ways," Samson said. "You know what they say. There's two kinds of farmers. There's the one that's got weeds and the one that's got money."

"There's the one that calls the county agent," Shavers said, "and the one that don't bother."

"Right," Samson said. "And there's the one that wants to sleep till seven o'clock in the morning and knock off work at three in the afternoon. He sells his farm to one of the big corporations."

There was the sound of children's voices from a back room at the Canyon County office. I walked down the hall and looked in. On a low platform at one end of the room was a demonstration kitchen, and sitting around a table at the other were ten little girls of eleven or twelve and a pretty young woman in white slacks and a sleeveless blue jersey. Most of the girls had pale-blond hair, most of them wore dresses, two wore glasses, one was fat, one was a foot taller than the others, and one had an arm in a sling. The woman was Lenora Fields, the other home economist, and this was a 4-H class.

". . . and Charlie," Mrs. Fields was saying, "is Charlie who?"

*"Calcium!"*

"That's right. And Charlie Calcium helps make what?"

*"Teeth and bones!"*

"And where is a good place to get calcium for good teeth and bones?"

*"Milk!"*

"Right. Now, Patty is Patty who?"

"Patty *Protein!"*

"And what does Patty Protein give?"

*"Energy!"*

"That's *right.* And where is a good place to . . ."

Arthur Walz, the area potato-and-onion specialist, and I had an early breakfast at Pollard's Drive-In Cafe. He is a tall, thin man of fifty with sandy-red hair and pale-blue eyes and freckles. We ordered bacon and eggs, and they were served, as usual, with hashed-brown potatoes. Hashed-brown potatoes are the grits of Idaho and the West. We ate to Bill Anderson on the jukebox singing "It Was Time for Me to Move On Anyway," helped ourselves at the cashier's desk to toothpicks and an after-dinner mint, and headed south in a gust of wind and a spurt of rain. Walz opened the glove compartment and got out a pair of sunglasses, and the sky began to clear.

"We've got a name for that," he said. "We call it an Idaho rainstorm. Two or three drops of water and a lot of wind, and then the sun comes out. I think we're going to have another nice hot sunny day for our trip. It's a trip I don't make any oftener than I have to. Owyhee County—the county where we're going—is the biggest county in my area, and it has the fewest people. As a matter of fact, it's one of the biggest counties in the United States. It's almost as big as the state of Massachusetts. But it's very rough country—mostly mountains and high desert. The only real crop is potatoes. There happen to be some very big producers, though, so I have to make a tour every couple of months or so. Those mountains up ahead are the Owyhee Mountains. 'Owyhee' is a phonetic spelling of "Hawaii.' We had a gold rush here in the early days, back in the eighteen-sixties, and it seems that a lot of the prospectors were Hawaiians. One big bunch of them had the misfortune to get massacred by the Indians. So the other prospectors started calling the place where it happened Owyhee."

We crossed the Snake River at the village of Marsing. Marsing was the beginning of Owyhee County. We stopped there for gas and to pick up the Owyhee County agent—a calm, square-built, gray-haired man named Glenn Bodily—and then continued south. It was a different countryside on this side of the river. The fertile Canyon County flats gave way to stony sagebrush hills and salt-grass hollows and occasional towering purple buttes. The river wound among the hills, and there were river meadows here and there, sometimes with a cow or two grazing in them. The air was hot and dry, and the sky was a hazy blue. A grove of trees appeared, like a mirage, ahead.

"That's Given's Hot Springs," Bodily said. "It used to be a famous resort."

"It was nice," Walz said. "People used to drive all the way down from Caldwell for a picnic in the shade of those old locust trees. Now all they want to do is stay at home with the air-conditioning on and watch the television."

The wilderness returned. Walz touched his lips with a protective salve, and pointed to a big falling-down frame building on the river-bank a mile or two away. "And there's a short history of Owyhee County," he said. "That started out as an Indian fort. Then they turned it into a ferry house. Then it was somebody's barn. Now it's nothing."

The road swung away from the river. We began to climb through an even wilder, even emptier countryside. And then, on a hilltop far ahead, a cluster of buildings came into view. A filling-station café. A one-story yellow brick building with a flagpole in front. Half a dozen houses. We passed a sign: "Murphy, Ida. Home of All-Girl Rodeo." We pulled off the road and into the filling station. A plump blond girl in jeans and boots watched us from a bench at the door of the café.

"Murphy is our Owyhee County seat," Bodily said. "And that is all it is. They put the seat here in the early days because this is more or less the middle of the county. It's about halfway between the two settled areas. That brick building there is the courthouse. There's nothing else but that and this and a post office. Well, let's go have us a cup of coffee." He opened the door. "Hello, Teddy."

"Hi, there," the girl said.

"Teddy," Walz said. "What's the population here now? About thirty?"

"Oh, no," she said. "I think it's up around seventy. But if you really want to know I'll find out. I'll count it."

We drank our scalding, watery coffee at the counter. The only other customers were two old men with stubbly sunken cheeks, wearing faded overalls and big hats and silently drinking beer. Behind the counter was a fat woman with a pile of bright-red hair. Teddy was waiting for us when we came out.

"I was wrong," she said. "It isn't seventy—it's only fifty-five. I guess a couple of families must have moved away."

After Murphy, the road began to worsen. There were potholes in the asphalt, and patches of cobblestone gravel. The mountains were edging closer. They rose higher and higher, with many thrusting peaks, but the slopes were green and gently rolling. "I've been chukar hunting all through there," Walz said. "Appearances are deceiving. It looks easy from here. But when you get up close—when you really get up in there—it's rough. You climb and climb and climb, and then you happen to stop and look back. You know you've been working, but when you look back down at all those shelves and rockslides, it scares you. It's a shock to see what you've been climbing through. And way, way down there is a tiny little speck, and you realize: My God, it's my car."

"This is all rough country in here," Bodily said. "It's pretty close to desolation. Some of Owyhee County is like Canyon County—all it needs is water. But this is different. The soil is different. Sagebrush is a good indicator of topsoil. Its size and abundance tell you something. But you don't see any sage along here. There's nothing but shad scale and rabbit brush. That white dust you see out there is bentonite clay. That's your soil, and it's almost impervious to water."

"They used to use bentonite to seal their irrigation ditches," Walz said. "It's almost as tight as cement. Bentonite is real bad news to farmers."

"You bet it is," Bodily said. "And a lot of farmers have had to find that out the hard way. I've seen them trying to plow it. But you know something, Art? That fork back there—I'm not too sure we're on the right road. You can get lost in this damn country."

"Not really," Walz said. "Somebody's bound to come along and find you in a day or two."

The road ran on through the featureless flats. There was nothing to see but the mountains and an occasional sculptured butte. The road turned and dipped and twisted down a hill. We crossed a little bridge with a trickle of creek below. Beyond the bridge were three or four houses. Then a ramshackle Pepsi-Cola store. Then a big stone Catholic church in a grove of poplar trees. Bodily gave a grunt and sat back.

"O.K., Art," he said. "We're in Oreana. But I haven't been down through here in quite some while."

"Oreana is one of our Basque colonies," Walz said. "They used to run sheep in here, but now it's mostly cattle. I don't know how they're making out."

"They do all right," Bodily said. "There's pretty good grazing on this side of the creek. They're interesting people. I remember a fellow just south of here who had a little stock operation. I came down with a specialist, and we looked over his range and his water and all the rest, and we worked out a nice expansion program for him. We were there for most of a day. And then he shook his head. 'I don't know,' he said. 'I think I'm happier the way I am.'"

Walz had two afternoon appointments. Both were with big potato growers whose holdings were on the high sagebrush plains beyond Oreana. We stopped on the way for a sandwich at the Black Sands

Cafe, in a tourist camp on the shore of a storage lake at the confluence of the Snake and one of its tributary rivers. The lake was a strange sight. Its waters were blue and sparkling in the sun, but the shores were arid desert. There were no trees, no greenery of shrub or grass. The gray, dusty desert brush ran down to the beach banks, down to the edge of the water. The only sign of life was six or seven coots floating at the mouth of a marshy cove.

After the lake, the potato fields—high and hot and windswept—had a look that was almost lush. The first of the farms was a corporate enterprise with some five thousand acres under cultivation. "We're running a little planting experiment here," Walz said. "Potato plants are usually grown about nine inches apart. We're trying them here at six inches. This is a big operation, with a big production, but they want to make it even bigger. That's why they're big." He and Bodily and a section lessee spent half an hour together—strolling along an endless field, stopping and talking, pointing and moving slowly on, nodding and frowning and tracing boot-toe patterns in the dust. I joined them for a while, and then went back to the shade of the car. The other farm was a two-thousand-acre fraction of a family operation. Walz was there to meet a group of salesmen and test two types of humidifier for use in a new potato-storage barn. I watched the tests with one of the family, a polite young man named Blaine Mecham. He had on the usual battered boots and an imitation-leopardskin cap. "No," he said. "I went to Utah State. My people are Latter-Day Saints. And I didn't go to ag school. After all, I was raised on a farm. I thought I'd do better to learn something I didn't already know. I majored in sociology, and my minor was ag economics. Then I worked for a year for the Bank of America in Fresno. Then I was ready to come back home and go to work. I hardly ever do any physical work myself. But I'm always here. I drive around and keep the men going. The market doesn't matter too much to us. We don't grow baking potatoes in this area. That's all done in the eastern part of the state, where it's high and cool. Our potatoes here grow too big for baking. We sell our crop by contract to the processor. If you've ever eaten any frozen French fries, you've probably eaten some of our potatoes. No, we don't live up here. We live in town—in Mountain Home."

We drove back to Marsing through the last heavy heat of the

desert afternoon. "I like to see a good operation," Walz said. "And we've seen a couple today. They aren't as common as some people like to think. The day of the hick is long gone. Farming is a real profession now. It demands a lot of a man. I've never seen a good farmer who wasn't above average in intelligence. He has to know how to handle men, he has to be able to plan, and he has to be able to manage land—he has to understand the land. I've known potato growers to get a yield of three hundred and fifty hundred-weight to the acre and still go belly up. They were thinking yield when they should have been thinking quality. Quality is work. You don't get quality by sitting around the café drinking coffee at ten o'clock in the morning. You have to live with the crop. That's one thing that hasn't changed. The best fertilizer is still the grower's shadow. We try to teach them that."

It was almost six o'clock when we dropped Bodily off at his office. The sun was low, and the air was beginning to cool. We crossed the river and climbed up through darkening orchards to the flats. The burgeoning fields began—mint and onions and alfalfa and beets and corn and beans—and there was a smell of blossomy sweetness. It was strange to think that this had once been a desert as forbidding as much of Owyhee County. I had a curious feeling that I had spent the day in the past. Owyhee County was a survival of the original Idaho. I had been given a glimpse of what Washington Irving saw for days on end when he passed this way in 1810. "It is a land," he wrote in "Astoria," his account of that journey, "where no man permanently resides; a vast uninhabited solitude, with precipitous cliffs and yawning ravines, looking like the ruins of a world; vast desert tracts that must ever defy cultivation and interpose dreary and thirsty wilds between the habitations of man."

Walz said, "Are you in a big hurry to get back to town?"

"Not particularly," I said. "Why?"

"I want to make a little detour for a minute."

He turned off the highway and down a dim gravel road. We drove slowly along for about a mile and pulled up at a twilit potato field. Walz opened his door and got out.

"I'll be right back," he said. "There's something I . . ."

He hopped across an irrigation ditch and climbed the bank and walked out to the edge of the field. I watched him standing there in the gathering dusk with his hands on his hips, looking down the long, sprouting rows. He came back and got under the wheel and started the engine.

"Something wrong?" I said.

"Wrong?" he said. "Oh, no. I just wanted to see— This field belongs to a fellow I've been working with. He had a little problem, and I've been a little worried. So I thought I'd just stop by and see. But it looks real nice, doesn't it? I think we're going to do all right."

# Forty Flights of Steps

Driving west not long ago through southern West Virginia, I stopped for the night at the mountain town of Welch. I stopped there for a night, and I stayed on for almost a week. Welch (pop. 4,149) is the seat of McDowell County, and McDowell County is Appalachia—the quintessence of Appalachia. It is rich in coal and poor in people. It is the home of a metallurgical coal favorably known throughout the industrial world as Pocahontas No. 3, and the birthplace of the federal food-stamp program. Its mines have never been more productive (or its working miners better paid), but since the mid-nineteen-fifties, when the continuous loader and other automated apparatuses were first introduced, the number of men employed in the McDowell County mines has fallen from twenty thousand to seven thousand. The population of the county has also sharply declined. It dropped from 98,887 in 1950 to 71,359 in 1960, and then to 50,400 in 1970, and many towns that were flourishing at the time of the Second World War are all but ghost towns now. I learned these facts in the course of my stay in Welch. They were not, however, what kept me there. I stayed because of the mountains.

McDowell County is as mountainous as my Long Island home is flat. It covers an area of five hundred and thirty-three square miles, and almost all of it is mountains—big, crowded, convoluted mountains. There is no ruggeder country anywhere east of the Rockies. The mountains are steep, with many cliffs and outcrop ledges, and the slopes are thickly grown with hickory and hemlock and oak and maple and groves of giant rhododendron. They rise—eight hundred, a thousand, fifteen hundred feet—to razorback ridges, and the valleys between are little more than ravines. Most of the valleys are river valleys, and most of the rivers are rushing mountain streams. The Tug Fork River, the biggest of these, has an average fall of ten feet to the mile. There is very little level land in the county (only two per cent of the total area has a slope of less than twelve feet in a hundred), and all of it is in the river valleys. So are all the towns. They are long, narrow towns—a mountainside and a river, a block of stores and houses, a railroad track, and another rising mountain. Welch is a maze of narrow streets and old brick buildings. It lies in a pocket of bottomland at the confluence of Elkhorn Creek, Brown's Creek, and the Tug Fork, and it is walled around with mountains.

I stayed in Welch at the Carter Hotel. Five stories high, built of orange brick and white marble, a comfortable relic of the coal boom of the twenties, the Carter occupies a corner at the intersection of McDowell Street, which runs north-south, and a steep, dead-end street called Bank Street. McDowell is one-way, just wide enough for two cars to move abreast, and flanked by four-foot sidewalks, but it is the Main Street of Welch. It follows the course of the Tug Fork River for most of its way through town. Across the river there is only a railroad track—a branch line of the Norfolk & Western. My room at the Carter was a corner room on the second floor, and it looked south along McDowell. Standing there on my first morning in town, I could see the U.S. Jewelers, the Flat Iron Drug Store, Bobo's Barbershop. Then came the mouth of an alley. Then the flank of a three-level parking garage. Then a five-story red brick building. Then the side of a wooded mountain. That was all. There was no sky. The mountain closed the view.

Every view in Welch is closed by a mountain. "Some of these mountains have names," Hobart Payne, the municipal recorder, told me in his office in City Hall. "They got around to naming some, and some they didn't bother. I guess we've got too many." City Hall fronts on Elkhorn Street, and Elkhorn Street fronts on Elkhorn

Creek, and across the creek is the rise of another mountain. "That mountain you're looking at, they call it Mitchell Mountain," Payne said. "Those buildings off to the right up there on the slope are the high school and the junior high. The mountain looks real pretty now, with the trees in leaf and the sun shining down and all. But you ought to see it in the winter. It makes the day pretty short. When I see the sun on those steps leading up to the school, I know it's almost time for lunch. The winter sun don't come over the top of Mitchell Mountain until just about half past ten. And, of course, we don't have it very long. The sun sets here on a winter day about half past two in the afternoon. As a matter of fact, the days aren't any too long here in Welch at any time of year. Sunrise this morning was five-fifteen, according to the almanac, but, if you happened to notice, it wasn't real light until almost seven-thirty."

Welch High School stands far above town but far below the summit of Mitchell Mountain. The steps leading up to it begin at a footbridge on Elkhorn Street which crosses Elkhorn Creek just opposite City Hall. It is a climb of fourteen steps from the end of the bridge to a narrow, hillside cross street of tall, hillside houses. This is Virginia Avenue. Ten more steps and a sidewalk ramp lead to a flight of forty-three steps, and these lead up to Maple Avenue, another cross street cut into the face of the mountain. A double stairway of sixteen steps circles up and around a terrace to the door of the school, which looks steeply down on Maple Avenue. "We've got four full stories here," William Belcher, the custodian, told me. "Five, counting the basement, where I've got my office. But I operate all over the building, and it's ninety-six steps from here on up to the top. Ninety-six steps, and I'm up there a dozen, fourteen times every day. I'll tell you something else. I grew up running the ridges. I was born out east of town, on Belcher Mountain. But I never knew what climbing was until I took this job. It don't seem to bother the kids. I guess the exercise is good for them. By the same token, this ought to be a healthy town. Everybody gets their exercise here. They can't very well avoid it. You can't walk anywhere in Welch without climbing up or down a hill. And you almost have to walk. I mean, you can't drive your car. Oh, you can drive it, but you can't find a place to park. Most of our streets aren't wide enough for parking. That's residential and business streets both. Some of them aren't even wide enough for sidewalks, and plenty have only one. The few streets here that are wide enough for parking, they're all set up with parking meters. So any place you find to park, it's going to cost you money. The only free parking in town is your own garage, if you've got one. Some people don't. They don't have the space. This town has its faults. These mountains are a problem. But it's like a fellow I had here one time used to say—how many places do you know where you can stand at the basement door and spit on the roof of a three-story house?"

Parking is a municipal monopoly in Welch. Only the town has had the ways and means to produce the necessary space. A plaque on the big parking garage on McDowell Street proclaims it to be "The First Municipally Owned Parking Building in the United States. Dedicated September, 1941." Two parking lots—one a little beyond the McDowell Street garage and the other across town—are also products of municipal ingenuity. Part of the McDowell Street lot is a shelf across the mouth of Elkhorn Creek. The other lot consists entirely of a platform spanning the Elkhorn for a distance of three hundred and twenty feet (with space for sixty cars), and it is engineered in such a way that water can flow harmlessly across it in time of flood. There are, in addition, a second parking garage (on Bank Street), a third parking lot, and several hundred metered parking spaces. The rates are low—paternalistically low (ten cents for an hour in a metered space, and off-street parking is even cheaper)—but the municipal parking system nevertheless produces an annual revenue of about a hundred and twenty thousand dollars. "We don't have a whole lot of crime in Welch," B. E. Dodson, the chief of police, told me. "Oh, we get a little breaking and entering, and sometimes a drifter comes through and maybe tries to steal a car. That's about the extent of it. I hope it stays that way. I mean, it better. I don't know how we'd manage otherwise. The Police Department operates the parking system, and that's practically a full-time job. That's why I've got my office here in the main garage. I've only got but twelve men, including my assistant, and we do it all—twenty-four hours a day. And the traffic. We got no time to spare for crime. The traffic here—Well, I've been to some real cities, and I've seen some traffic problems. But you take a Friday afternoon right here, with the town full of folks looking to spend their paychecks and their food stamps and their unemployment and their Social Security and their Black Lung and their everything else—I call that traffic. And speeding. You wouldn't think it was possible to speed on the kind of streets we have in Welch, but they do. The kids do. They even some of them drag. You know Matney's junk yard, out south of town? They won't even take your car anymore. They got enough."

There are six automobile agencies in Welch. They serve the town and most of McDowell County. The largest agency (with two show-rooms) is Hall Chevrolet-Oldsmobile, Inc. "We also handle Jeeps," John R. Hall, the president, told me. "This is good country for Jeeps. It's good country for any kind of car. I can sell all the Oldses I can get. These people are crazy about cars. We sell around three hundred and fifty new and seven hundred and fifty used cars a year. We sold a hundred and ten last month alone. And the other dealers— they aren't hurting, either. People really love cars here. Go up a hollow and look at the houses. They're pretty sorry, most of them. But look at the cars out front. Count them. If there's five in the family over sixteen years of age, they've got five cars. A car is something they can spend their money on. It's something to do. They like to drive. They like to drive it hard. They don't care that the roads are narrow and winding and full of holes. You can hit a hole *this* deep on any highway in the county. But they don't care. They don't let that bother them. These people can total a car like nobody else in the world. We've got two tow trucks here and we can't begin to keep up with the wrecks. Look at that red Camaro out there in back. Look at that front end. I don't know if it's even worth repairing. And, shoot, it isn't more than four months old."

Accidents are a commonplace on the hillside streets and switchback roads of Welch and the surrounding county. I read about them every day in the Welch *Daily News* ("Two Injured in Highway Wreck"), and the signs are everywhere—a streak of sudden tire skids, a broken guardrail cable, a totalled car at the bottom of a ravine. One afternoon on Warren Street—a riverside street so narrow that I had to back up half a block to let an approaching car get past me—I counted the splattered corpses of a dog, a cat, two squirrels, and a rabbit. "You can always tell an out-of-stater by the way he handles his car," a state trooper assigned to McDowell County told me. "He creeps. He brakes. He's scared to death of those drops. Some visitors park their car and won't touch it again until it's time to leave. The natives understand the roads. They think they do, anyway. Still, we average maybe thirty accidents a month around the county that are serious enough to call the police. The funny thing is they're very few of them collisions. Most of our accidents, and practically all our fatalities, involve just one vehicle." There was a report of such an accident in the *Daily News* on my second day in Welch. It read:

Tony Joe (Tommy) Craig, 40, of Welch, miraculously escaped death or serious injury early this morning when a car he was driving plunged several hundred feet off Hobart Street and down a hillside, lodging between a stone wall and the Joe Rucci home on lower McDowell Street, Welch Police Lt. Adolph Bary reported.

The vehicle was demolished, and local police and members of the fire department worked for almost an hour before freeing Craig from the twisted wreckage. He was rushed to Stevens Clinic, where he was under observation for a neck injury. He is also reported to have suffered some cuts and bruises.

Bary said he and Patrolman Estil Halsey are continuing an investigation in an effort to learn the cause of the accident. The 1954 Chevrolet bounced off a high rock cliff and then rolled down the hillside. The incident occurred about 3:30 A.M., while Craig was enroute home from downtown Welch, Bary said.

I read the report as it came from the press at the offices of the *Daily News*. "I'd call that a little unusual," C. H. Hardison, the managing editor, told me. "They don't usually survive. But we get a lot of those over-the-cliff accidents. We've got a lot of cliffs. I had an accident like that happen at my house a few years ago. It was early in the morning, in the winter, in February. I live out south, on Summers Street, down by the river, and a woman came along on the street above and hit some ice on a curve and went through the wire fence they have there and came down my back-yard hill and knocked down an apple tree I'd finally got to grow there and slammed into the back of my house. She hit the house at the second floor and then came sliding down, and she took the bathroom window and a whole wall of aluminum siding with her. I called the fire department and the police, and they came, and all they said was 'Get a blanket.' "

I walked up to Hobart Street for a look at the scene of Tony Joe Craig's miraculous escape. To get there, I climbed a street (Court Street) so steep that the sidewalk began and ended as a flight of steps. There are houses—most of them four-story houses—standing shoulder to shoulder on the upper side of Hobart Street on terraced lots secured by a twelve-foot stone retaining wall, and the front doors are reached by flights of twenty and thirty, and even forty, steps. A few of the houses (six in a block of twenty) have garages—little caves dug into the mountain and framed by the retaining wall. Hobart Street is eighteen feet wide, and there is a three-foot sidewalk along the upper side. The other side of the street is a drop of at least three hundred feet to a thrust of rooftops below. I expected to locate the scene by finding a gap in a fence or guardrail. But there is no fence or guardrail the length of Hobart Street. There is only a curbing about four inches high. I never found where the car went over. It could have jumped the curbing at almost any point from one end of the street to the other.

The mayor of Welch is a tall, thin Republican (in a Democratic town) named William B. Swope, and he is also its leading real-estate broker. His real-estate business occupies the ground floor of a three-story brick building on McDowell Street. The upper floors are divided into apartments. "You won't find many buildings here in Welch that don't have a couple of floors of apartments up above," he told me. "People have to have someplace to live. I've done all right in the real-estate business, but real estate is a problem here. We've got a lot of mountains, but we don't have any land, and what we have is rarely on the market. The first thing you want to understand is that most of the land in McDowell County—well, a good third of it, anyway—is owned by just one company. I mean the Pocahontas Land Corporation, and the Pocahontas Land Corporation is a subsidiary of the Norfolk & Western Railway Co. They don't do any mining. They lease the rights to the coal companies and to people like U.S. Steel. They're ready to lease, but they hate to sell. The other big owners—Berwind Land Corporation and Consolidation Coal Com-

pany—they think pretty much the same. They will almost never sell
you any land in fee. The most you can buy is just the surface. They
retain the mineral rights. They're not going to let you have what
might be a rich seam of coal. That's only sensible. And the reason
they don't like to sell even the surface is this. This country is riddled
with coal mines. There are miles of mines right under the city of
Welch. And they're always opening new ones. Well, suppose you
built a house and the land underneath gave way and the house fell
into a mine. They don't want to worry about lawsuits. But the result
is a hell of a problem. We don't even own a city dump. We rent
five acres in a hollow out west of town. The only sewage-treatment
plant in the county is one that U.S. Steel built out at Gary, five
miles south of here. I've got plans for one here in Welch. I've got
my eye on a site at the north end of town where we could build
an oxidation ditch. Our sewage now goes into the river. I was able
to put in a pipe that carries it downstream, out of town. But we'll
solve those problems. We've got a good hundred years of coal still
left to mine. The big problem is housing. You've seen the houses
here in town. There's no such thing as level land, and if you've got
a lot as big as seventy-five by a hundred feet you've practically got
an estate. I know houses that aren't fit for a hog. Dirty. Fallen down.
Hung on the side of a mountain halfway up some hollow. But people
will jump at the chance to buy them and fix them up. We've got a
hospital here that's offering a guarantee of fifty thousand a year for
a doctor. They can't get one. They drive into town with their wives,
and she won't even get out of the car. The hills and the roads and
no place to build a nice big house—it scares them all away. But
God damn it. They don't realize. This place could be another
Switzerland."

Mayor Swope himself is comfortably housed. He lives in a nice
big stone house with a double gallery across the front, and it stands
on a shelf of terraced lawn high up on Mitchell Mountain. I saw it
in his company a day or two after our meeting. We approached it
along a climbing, winding private road that ended at the door of a
garage cut into the mountain slope. The house was directly below
the garage, and below the house—far, far below—lay all of Welch.
A flight of (thirty-four) stone steps led down to the house. "My
grandfather built this house in 1903," Swope told me. "Welch was

just beginning then, and there were a lot of highly skilled Italian stonemasons around. 'Tallies,' they called them. The retaining walls you see all over town, the Tallies built them all. Beautiful work. But a lost art now. Now it's all poured concrete, and it ain't worth a damn. It won't last—it doesn't have the weight, it doesn't have the strength. The Tallies built this house. They dug the stone out of the hillside here. They shot and chipped and did it all by hand. It's still as sound as solid rock. I haven't had to do hardly a thing. I *did* put in our road. In my grandfather's time and in my father's time and until not too many years ago, the only way to get to this house was from the street below. That's Maple Avenue way down there, and there are a hundred and sixty-three steps between the street and our front door. My wife and I and our two boys and a girl, we all walked up and down those steps every day of our lives, but we had a winch and a basket on a cable for packages and groceries and stuff. We heated the house with coal. Everything is natural gas here now. That's another thing I've done as mayor, and the city is a little cleaner. Nobody burns coal now except a few miners. They get it at reduced rates by contract. Pocahontas No. 3 is too expensive to burn for heat. Twenty dollars a ton. They only use it for coke. But in the old days you burned coal or nothing, and getting it up the mountain to this house was a problem. My grandfather solved it by having his own mine. A lot of people did the same. Our mine is back there under the garage. It runs back into the mountain for about a thousand feet, and we had a man to dig it for us. He pushed it out on a car on a little track. I walled our mine up ten years ago. We had a miner killed in there. I'll never open it again—not unless I need a bomb shelter."

Most of the best houses in Welch are old houses, and most of them are acquired by inheritance. Few of them ever appear on the open market. "I guess you could say we inherited our house," Rollo L. Taylor, the publisher of the *Daily News*, told me. "We wouldn't be here if we hadn't. We're not natives. My wife is from Alabama, and I was working on the paper in Spartanburg, down in South Carolina, when we heard that the *Daily News* was coming up for sale. That was in 1963, and we had a baby and we wanted a paper of our own. We came up here and looked the situation over, and everything looked all right—except for a place to live. You've seen some of the houses here. But we were lucky. The publisher of the paper wanted to move away, so we ended up buying his house along with the paper. It's a good brick house, well built and plenty of room (we've got two children now), and we even have a little lawn. A *level* lawn." Other couples new to Welch have had a less hospitable welcome. They have found that the acquisition of a house costs more than merely money. It also calls for patience, vigilance, and an elastic adaptability. "We moved here about ten years ago," Mrs. Edward Jarvis, Jr., told me. "My husband is an inspector-at-large for the State Department of Mines, and we were living up in Fayette County. Then he was transferred to this area. He came down first. He got a room in a motel and started looking around. It took him a month to find an apartment. It wasn't a real apartment. It was just four rooms on the top floor of a house on Court Street. So I came down and we moved in and I began looking for a real place to live—a house. I looked for eight years—eight solid *years*—and then a house turned up out in Junior Poca, out toward Gary. It was the very first house that became available in all those years, and we didn't hesitate. We took it. It's built on a fifteen-degree slope, and there's a long climb up to the front door, but we've got seven rooms, and it's wonderful to finally settle down."

There are about a dozen places to eat in Welch. Most of them are lunchrooms, diners, or drive-ins. I had most of my meals at a clean, well-lighted café (with a horseshoe counter, and tables with tablecloths, and booths around the walls) called the Mountaineer Restaurant. It occupies the ground floor of a two-story building on a corner of McDowell Street, just down the block from the Carter Hotel, and it is owned and operated by a Welchian of Italian descent named Quinto Bary. One morning, on my way to breakfast there, I happened to look up, and saw that the building was *not* a two-story building. It was a one-story building with a one-story house—a bungalow with a low-pitched roof—on top. The building was red brick, and the house was clapboard, painted red.

I had my breakfast and then looked around and found Bary sitting alone in a booth with a cup of coffee. "Oh, that," he told me. "That was all my wife. She got the brainstorm. We had a house—a regular house—but it wasn't what we wanted. But you can't buy a lot to build on in this town. Even if there was one, it would cost too much.

We had this building, though, and my wife got to thinking. It was a good sound building, and the size was big enough—thirty-four by seventy-five feet. I went to a builder and talked about the cost of building something on the roof. The price he gave me, I decided to take a long gamble and build it myself, and I got a real good carpenter that was also willing to try. Weight was one problem, of course. And then there was how to get the material up there on the roof. For that, we built a ramp, like a switchback road, in the back. And to keep down the weight we used aluminum siding. That isn't clapboard, it's all aluminum. We worked out a lot of tricks for convenience. The windows are aluminum, and they lift out for washing. We couldn't stand the weight of a furnace, and the restaurant furnace here wouldn't handle the load, so we heat the house with electricity. We've got three bedrooms, two bathrooms, a big living room, a kitchen, a utility room, and plenty of closets. We've even got a terrace, like a roof garden, in the back. The only thing we haven't got that I'd like to have is a fireplace—too heavy. And the only trouble is that there's too much shade and it's hard to get anything to grow real good up there on the terrace."

There are no farms in McDowell County, and no commercial orchards. A few countrymen keep bees. Driving the mountain roads, I would sometimes see on the slope of a hollow a cluster of white box hives and mistake them for a moment for a row of headstones in a family burying ground. (There *are* a number of family burying grounds in McDowell County, but only two cemeteries. No room. One of the two, a hillside acre near Gary—half Protestant, half Catholic—has long since reached capacity. The only operating cemetery in the county is Iaeger Memorial Cemetery, on a long, climbing point of land at a bend in the Tug Fork River, just below a hamlet called Roderfield.) Even flower or vegetable gardens are rare. They are almost unheard of in town—in Welch. Few householders have space enough in the sun for more than a border of roses or a terraced row of tomatoes. Edward Jarvis, the mine inspector, is one of these. "I've got the room," he told me. "And the slope isn't too bad. I've had pretty good luck with tomatoes and green beans and peppers and lettuce and even watermelon. The only trouble is the mountains. I've got an eastern exposure, and my garden gets the sun for only about three hours—from around eleven o'clock in the morning until two in the afternoon."

One of the biggest holders of tillable land in McDowell County is a wholesale-grocery salesman named Harry Wells. Wells lives a few miles south of Welch, on the road to Gary, and he has around five acres of level bottomland on the east bank of the Tug Fork River. "Let's stop here in the shade," he said to me. "This old cherry tree is a lifesaver on a hot day. And we get some hot days. It's nice and open in this part of the valley, so we're blessed with plenty of sun. Some of these hollows, they're no better than caves. Well, there's my land. It runs on down around that bend, and it's all good loam. No clay. No rocks. No coal. It's been tended for a good long time. I'm sixty-three years old, and my daddy was tending it before I was born. My daddy was a farmer—one of the last in the county. He used to grow corn on that hillside up there cross the road. You look like you're wondering how. Well, those days are gone forever. You can't plow land that steep with a tractor. My daddy plowed with a mule. I've never really farmed myself, but I used to tend this bottom. But then I got a better idea. You know how folks live in Welch. They haven't got room enough to hardly even stretch, but a lot of them have that natural urge to plant a garden and see things grow. So I started renting out this land in little patches. I charged them ten dollars for a big enough strip, and I supply the water. I guess I could rent out twice as much land as I've got. Half of Welch does their gardening here. You know Rollo and Annis Taylor? Well, they've been growing stuff here for years. On a summer weekend, this place of mine is full of folks all down on their knees enjoying themselves. Some of them, they'll try anything. Mustard greens. Kale. Broccoli. Okra. Why, there's even some of them growing herbs."

I saw one other garden during my stay in McDowell County. This garden is also out toward Gary, and it is cultivated by a man named H. V. Ashley. Ashley owns and operates a big yellow clapboard railroad boarding house in a Norfolk & Western switchyard on the west bank of the Tug Fork. His place is bounded on the back and sides by acres of sidings and block-long strings of hopper-bottom coal cars, and on the front by the river. A swinging footbridge with a plank floor leads across the river to the road. (There are many such bridges in McDowell County. "I understand from my undertaker friends that there's nothing like a funeral where you have to carry the coffin across a swinging bridge," Rollo Taylor told me.) I had lunch one day at Ashley's place. The floor was grained and gritty with coal dust, and I ate on a stool at a counter—with a crowd of big, laughing, shouting, starving railroad men—to the rumble of locomotives and the clatter and shriek of hoppers. Lunch was pork chops, red beans, corn bread, and Dr. Pepper. After lunch, Ashley took me off in a four-wheel-drive pickup truck to see his garden. It was across the river, across the road, up a steep, sliding, coal-slag cart track, across a cascading brook on a railless bridge of railroad ties, and up a long hollow. We stopped near the head of the hollow at a garden plot about the size of a tennis court. Just beyond the garden were a little square brick building and a huge cylindrical pipe, like a silo on its side. The mouth of the pipe faced down the hollow, and it was fitted with a wire-mesh guard. Through the grille and down across the garden came a driving dynamo hum. "They call this Shaft Hollow," Ashley told me, "and that pipe there is the shaft. It's a ventilator shaft—the outflow from a U.S. Steel Company mine back under that mountain. The shaft is why I've got this garden here. The air blowing out of the mine is a constant sixty degrees, and that makes this end of the hollow like a greenhouse. We're up fairly high here— a couple of thousand feet—but I can put my garden in early. At least a month before the rest of them. And it produces long past frost. You wouldn't believe the crops I get. My sugar corn is six or seven feet high, compared to the average here of maybe four, and the first crop of beans I got last year was over a hundred bushels. I don't own this land, of course. It all belongs to Pocahontas, and they lease it out to U.S. Steel. But they don't care, either one of them, if I use it. They're only interested in coal. Listen how quiet it is up here. You don't hear nothing but that fan. This is what I call peaceful. It's soothing. Well, I'm going to drive you back a different way. It's around the side of the mountain, and you'll get a real nice view—right down on top of my place. My God, I remember one night. I was sitting at home and I heard a noise and I looked out and saw a light shining up on the road. I looked again, and it was a car laying on its back and with one of the headlights shining. I ran out and up to the road and opened the door—and it was my best buddy laying dead across the wheel. He lived up this hollow and he knew the road, but I guess he did something wrong. I'll show you the place where he missed and went over."

On my way back to Welch, I picked up two hitchhiking teenage boys. They hailed me from an unpaved block of houses just north of Ashley's place, and I stopped and they climbed into the front seat beside me. They both wore bluejeans and striped sneakers, and one of them had a basketball under his arm. They weren't going in to town. Heck, no. They only wanted a lift down the road about a mile. They were local boys; their fathers both worked for U.S. Steel.

"My dad don't actually work in the mines," the boy with the basketball said. "He don't like it underground. He says it gives him that whatchamacallit phobia. What he does, he's a car dropper. He unloads the cars that come out of the mine."

"That don't bother my dad," the other boy said. "He likes the weather in there. It's always nice and cool. And the pay is good. It's better, anyway. The mines aren't like they used to be, I guess—the conditions. They're safer, anyway."

"My dad says things are a whole lot better," the first boy said. "And cleaner, too. He says the company used to dump the water from the coal washers in the river, but now they can't. The state won't let them. He says when he was a boy they used to dive in the river at a swimming hole they had, and he'd come up through like a foot of solid coal dust."

"I might go into the mines," the other boy said. "That's the only thing that would ever keep me here. I don't know. But the pay is good. And I kind of like these mountains. I sure don't like it where it's flat. I was up at my cousin's for a while last summer in Delaware, and it really made me feel funny. It was so flat. The only trouble here is there isn't nothing to do. There isn't no place you can go with a girl and park. Where you can be alone. What you have to do is go all the way out to the movie at Kimball—to the drive-in."

"That costs money," the first boy said.

"That's what I mean," the other boy said.

"Yeah," the first boy said. He turned back to me. "Well, thanks a lot. You can let us out at the store up there."

The store was an unpainted shed in a roadside niche in the mountain wall. The only window was broken, and there was a padlock hanging open on the door. Above the door was a homemade sign: "No Lawn Mowers Repaired Here." But the store wasn't where they were going. I watched them walk around the car and across to a little spit of land on the other side of the road. It was just big enough to accommodate a nosed-in car, and there was a drop all around of twenty feet or more to the river bottom below. At the end of the spit, a couple of feet from the edge, stood a ten-foot post with a plywood backboard at the top and a rusty basketball ring.

# The Good News

For the law of the Spirit of life in Christ Jesus
has set me free.

*—Romans 8:2.*

It is a warm Sunday morning in spring, and I am in Orange (pop.
6,188), an old mill town in northwestern Massachusetts, sitting alone
in a golden-oak pew in the Central Congregational Church, with
the sun burning blue and green and yellow through a wall of memorial
stained-glass windows. The service has progressed from organ prelude
to hymn to invocation to offertory to prayer to Scripture lesson
(". . . and let us consider how to stir up one another to love and
good works"), and now the minister is standing high in the tower of
his golden-oak pulpit. He is the Reverend Edward Thomas Hougen,
a slight young man in a billowing black robe, with long blond hair
falling almost to his shoulders, and he looks down in silence for a
moment at his congregation of some sixty worshippers. I had just
met Hougen. I had come up to Orange to see him only yesterday,
and had dined last night with him and his wife at the parsonage,
and now, as he began to speak, I heard him with surprise. His voice
from the pulpit was not a pulpit voice. It was his natural voice—
easy, halting, conversational. He spoke as he had spoken at dinner.

". . . sticks and stones," he was saying. "And there are many other familiar phrases that also bring to mind a negative and destructive picture. One of these is 'stirring people up.' We think of a lynch mob, a crowd of demonstrators—any angry group—as stirred up. And we avoid stirring people up. We're afraid, because we know that just below the surface, waiting to be released, are a lot of hostile emotions. It's easy to arouse our negative feelings. Some politicians make a specialty of it. And because we know about these feelings and how easy it is to arouse them, we work very hard to avoid or bank down our emotions. Especially in church. In our work in church. We don't like discord, we dread disharmony, and so we try to avoid any emotionally charged issues. Controversy upsets us. So we table divisive problems. But that doesn't deal with them; they don't go away. And not only that. The effort it takes to avoid them drains us of energy to deal with anything else. We all know how exhausting it is to entertain difficult relatives or people we don't much like. And for lots of us our involvement in the church is too much like that kind of entertaining. It's a duty we go through. Then we're glad to go home and take off our Sunday clothes and put on our real selves. We're so afraid of our negative feelings that we let them block our positive, constructive emotions. And instead of our church life being an intense, passionate, involving experience, it becomes a bland and empty exercise. But it is clear from Scripture that as Christians we are called upon to *get* involved, to stir up one another, to express our real emotions. We don't have to be afraid of dissension. Things aren't going to fall apart. God is *not* going to abandon us— whatever we do. We are His; we are His instrument. It is right for us to stir each other up. Let's face hostility. Let's confront it. To express it is to dissipate it. Stirring up can be constructive—it *is* constructive. The sticks and stones that can break our bones, the sticks and stones that can be used as weapons, are the same sticks and stones that we build with."

The rising roar of the organ filled the sanctuary. It rumbled into the opening bars of "Lord of All Hopefulness," and the congregation stood and sang. Hougen pronounced the benediction. There was a pause. Then he moved quickly across the chancel and down the steps, and walked smiling up the aisle.

We came out of the grim red brick block of Athol Memorial Hospital, a community hospital that serves the Orange area, and headed back across the parking lot to Hougen's little blue Simca. It was late Monday afternoon, and hot. Hougen had his hair pushed back behind his ears, and his jacket—a green-and-yellow madras jacket—was slung over his arm. "I think these hospital visits are important," he said. "I think they do some good. I hope so, anyway, because they're just about the hardest thing I do. I know sick people want to talk about their sickness, but the questions I have to ask still seem like nosy questions to me. Especially in a ward, where there are other patients listening. Like just now. But, of course, the worst is when the person is a little deaf. Shouting out a prayer in that setting—it's embarrassing. I don't mind the hospital part. I mean hospitals per se don't bother me. My father was a doctor. He was a general practitioner in Sheboygan, Wisconsin. That's where I was born and raised. There was a time when I thought seriously of being a doctor myself."

"What happened?" I said.

Hougen laughed. He tossed his jacket into the back of the car and slid behind the wheel. "I also thought of being a drama critic," he said. "Or maybe a director—a movie director. I'm still almost fanatically interested in movies. That's the worst thing about living here in Orange. No movies. But I can hardly remember a time when I wasn't in some way involved with religion. We had a minister in our Congregational church at home—Wilford Evans, a really great man. I always found the church more intellectually stimulating than school. He was really exciting. He was very honest. He gave straight answers to everything. No party line. And he had an almost cosmic grasp of things. He raised questions about things like the nature of God and forgiveness and faith—all that. I assaulted him with ideas all through high school, and he would refine them and clarify them, and then raise other questions. He was different. I had a friend at school, a boy who was a Lutheran. We used to discuss things, and one day we came up with the question 'Is it a sin to swear?' " Hougen looked amazed. "That was only fifteen years ago—did we actually talk like that? It sounds like another century. But, anyway, we decided to ask our ministers about it. I went to Mr. Evans, and he just shrugged and said it was hardly a serious sin—maybe venial, at most. What it really was, he said, was just bad taste. So I went back to my friend and told him, and he told me what *his* minister had said. *His* minister told *him* not to see me anymore. If I had been brought up in that kind of church or by that kind of minister, I probably wouldn't be a minister today."

We drove through the red brick town of Athol and turned off on the road to Orange. It was a single-lane highway lined with filling stations and drive-ins and boarded-up roadhouses with deep, dark woods behind. "I was quite skeptical about religion," Hougen said. "What interested me were the intellectual questions. My commitment to the answers—to the Christian faith—wasn't very strong. But I was going to church camps all through those high-school summers. I liked the experience of community and the atmosphere of closeness. It was all very upbeat. And then, at a conference the summer before I went off to Harvard, I met a woman missionary from India—Lillian Picken. She was really responsible for my being a minister. When she spoke, she had the audience entranced. She was a truly charismatic kind of woman. She had an aura of openness and aliveness—a joyfulness. I talked with her, and I asked her what was her secret—what made her so different? She said it was Jesus Christ. She said that God can take your life and remake it and make it exciting and alive. She said that you can come to know God and Jesus as a person. Well, I sure wanted what she had. I had many doubts, and I knew that this was the simple, basic evangelical appeal—nothing to do with the metaphysical. But I believed her. And later that week I asked God to take my life as He had taken hers. I had never wanted anything more. Then I went to sleep, and the next morning— This sounds like a fairy tale, but the next morning I felt different. I felt different about who I was. And God and Jesus were both real to me. It was no philosophical thing—it was a real force. I looked at the Bible and for the first time really understood it. It was a classic conversion experience. It was the most profound and vivid and real experience of my entire life. It turned me on to the Christian faith. I knew I wanted to spend my life in the faith—in the ministry. It was just like the words in the hymn: *'I leapt alive.'*"

We came into Orange, and the highway became East Main Street. We passed the shops and foundries of the Rodney Hunt Company, manufacturers of industrial machinery; the battlements of the National Guard Armory; the blazoned windows of the Piggly Wiggly. We turned left at the traffic light onto South Main Street (North Main Street was to the right and West Main Street was straight ahead) and into the twilight of an avenue of great, arching maples. We passed the Central Congregational Church. We passed the Witty Funeral Home. The parsonage, where I had left my car, was a block or two farther on—a big white clapboard house on a corner, with a veranda across the front and a bow window on the side. Hougen parked in the driveway in back. We went up to the kitchen door, and Mrs. Hougen, slim and blond and smiling, unlatched the screen and let us in. The latch was near the top of the door, out of reach of the Hougens' daughter, a three-year-old named Sarah. Their second child, a boy named Edward, Jr., was only a few months old at the time of my visit.

"I want you to see him," Mrs. Hougen said to me. "He's a beautiful boy." She looked at Hougen and laughed. "All the time I was pregnant, Edward went around telling people, 'We're hoping for either a boy or a girl, but we'll be happy with whatever we get.' "

"That's right," Hougen said. "And now we'll be happy with a couple of beers."

When I left the parsonage, I drove on out South Main Street for a couple of blocks, and pulled into a Mobil station. The attendant came out and unlimbered the pump.

"Been up seeing the Reverend, eh?"

"The news travels fast," I said.

"Well," he said, "I guess I know most of the cars in town."

It was a gray shingle house set close to the street, with a patch of grassless yard and a couple of steps leading up to a narrow porch. We climbed the steps and Hougen knocked, and a dark-haired woman opened the door a crack.

"We're looking for Mrs. Russell," he said. "Mrs. Sarah Russell."

"Around back," the woman said, and closed the door.

We went around back and knocked on another door. It was opened by a short, stout woman with thin white hair and thick eyeglasses. Beyond her I could see a crowded living room—overstuffed chairs, a sofa upholstered in plum-colored plush, cabinets full of glassware and china, tables with vases of artificial flowers, many family photographs, a television set.

"Mrs. Russell?" Hougen said. "I'm the Reverend Edward Hougen. I called you yesterday and—"

"Oh, yes. Of course. Come in, come in. I do so wish I could come to church more often. Why don't you take that big chair, Reverend? It isn't just a matter of transportation. My son is very good about taking me out for a drive in his automobile. But I just can't hurry enough to get ready for church in time. I had that bad operation, you know, and that cataract trouble, but I think I do pretty well for ninety-one years old. I have seven living children. This house belongs to one of my sons. He and his wife have the front, and I have my own place here in back. I'm close but not in with them. I like company, but I like to be able to shut the door. My daughter-in-law is very good about bringing me a nice hot dinner when I feel like something hot. I have seven living children and thirty grandchildren and seventy-three great-grandchildren and thirty great-great-grandchildren."

"Well," Hougen said, "I must say—"

"One of my sons is beginning to get cataract trouble," Mrs. Russell said. "It seems as if it's the fair-haired ones that have that trouble. I was a blonde. That's a picture up there of me and my husband. That was taken fifty years ago, and you can see that I was quite blonde. When I was little, I was a little snow-head. I've got my Social Security, and I've always been what they call careful. I've had this furniture since 1943. I was never one to let things go to ruin. I got quite a bargain on this rug—and there isn't a bare spot on it yet. I had my winter coat for seventeen years. Now that we've got that raise in Social Security, I may be able to make a little contribution to the church. I do wish I could come to church more often. I don't miss the television as much as I thought I would. There's such a sameness in the programs. I only wish— I wonder if you could come sometime and give me Communion, Reverend?"

"I'd be very happy to," Hougen said. "Perhaps I could some day next—"

"Yes," Mrs. Russell said. "I do so wish I could come to church more often."

"I don't mean economically," Hougen said. We were sitting in a booth at the Koffee Hut. We had left Mrs. Russell a few minutes earlier and had stopped for a cup of coffee. "Although there's that, too," he said. "I mean emotionally depressed. I haven't been in Orange very long, but I get the feeling that the people here have such a negative self-image. They seem to feel that they're going no place. In some way that they don't quite understand, they're thwarted. Maybe it's the same everywhere. It may have been the same at my first church—down in South Hadley. But I was only the associate there. Anyway, the problem is one that is certainly within the scope of the church. It's the function of the church to help people understand who they are, to raise their concept of self. I wouldn't be in the ministry if I didn't feel that. Christianity is involved with the real world. I went to Harvard in a very mystical state of mind. My conversion experience was so new. I didn't want to risk it. I was afraid of any conflict with the rational. I rejected all of my intellectuality. The first guys I got to know were spiritualistic, evangelistic, semi-fundamentalist. One of them was a guy called Buster. We were talking in his room one day, and he told me about an experience he'd had. He'd been walking along the river, and God appeared and said, 'I love you, Buster.' I began to feel uncomfortable. And then Buster opened a drawer and got out a box of Chunky candy bars and gave me one. That made me feel even more uncomfortable. I felt he was involving me in a symbolic act of some kind. I resented it. And I never liked Chunky bars anyway.

"But that started a change. I got onto Kierkegaard, and he gave me some good philosophical support. I decided that God had given me my good mind to use. He expected me to use it. If God was real—and I knew He was—I needn't be afraid to venture out beyond my conversion experience. It would be a lack of faith to hold back. Christianity isn't intended to force us into a mold or pattern—into an image of a faithful person. It's just the opposite. It isn't rigidity. It isn't not drinking or not smoking or not sleeping with girl friends. It isn't a bloodless fellowship. Christian faith is freeing. It's freedom from the fear of death, from the fear of self-knowledge, from the inadequacies of self, from the pressure and need to win the love and approval of others. The Christian experience is to realize that God loves you because you are you—because you are His. The unbeliever is always striving. Am I loved? Am I lovable? Am I of value? Because we all know that love is freeing. All love is freeing, but divine love is completely freeing. That sounds a little like a Coke ad. But it's true. I know that the traditional ways of understanding God have lost their meaning for a lot of people. They're uncomfortable with the concept of God as Father. The Christian gospel seems to embarrass them, and to justify it they try to find faith in abstract terms. The 'God is dead' notion was going strong when I was at seminary. That notion came out of the academic setting; it's an intellectual sophistication. Or was—there isn't much left of it now. I heard Paul Tillich speak once while I was at Harvard. One of the students asked him, 'Do you believe in God?' His answer was typical. He said, 'What do you mean by God?' But what have you gained by substituting for 'God' a phrase like 'Ground of Being' or 'Being Itself'? Christian faith isn't a problem in semantics. That isn't much help to real people working in a real world. Crises of faith aren't crises of language. God as Father has real meaning. We all know what a father—a real father—should be."

Hougen finished his coffee and pushed the cup away. "I met a man at a party here," he said. "We got to talking, and I asked him what he did. He said he taught philosophy. Then, later on, it turned out that he was a part-time instructor at some community college—he taught one course. What he really was, was a minister. He was a Lutheran minister in one of the neighboring towns. I was appalled. I wondered what kind of a minister he could be if he felt that way about it. It made me feel sick."

Mrs. Murchie was an elderly woman with dark-brown hair, and she was wearing a lavender housedress. "Lillian!" she called. "We've got company. Here's Mr. Hougen and a friend." Beaming, she led us across the hall to the living room  It was a small room crowded with heavy furniture and piles of magazines everywhere *(Family Circle, Woman's Day, McCall's, TV Guide)* and a big television set in a corner. A younger woman, of about fifty, was reclining on a sofa. She wore a green housedress and heavy black stockings, and her hair was almost white. She put out her hand and smiled.

"Well, Miss Murchie," Hougen said. "How have you been?"

"I'm better," she said. "I still black out, but I'm really much better."

"I know one thing," Mrs. Murchie said. "She always looks on the sunny side."

"Do you know how I sleep?" Miss Murchie said. "I have this circulatory problem, you know, and I'm always cold. I sleep in a long woollen nightgown and I wear gloves and I have pillows at my feet. I look laid out. I tell Mother to put a bouquet of flowers in my hands, and then if I don't wake up I'll be all ready for Brud Witty."

"Lillian," Mrs. Murchie said. "Don't talk like that. I can't stand those jokes. Do you know, when she has a spell I have to pound her on the back until my hand hurts."

"It hurts me, too," Miss Murchie said. "But you know what they say—you can't kill an old maid."

"It's your faith, Lillian," Mrs. Murchie said.

Hougen hung up the phone and sat back and ran his fingers through his hair. We were sitting in his big, bare, golden-oak study at the church. "They'll be here in about fifteen minutes," he said. "I think maybe I'd better see them alone. But it won't take too long. Then we'll go down and see what's happening in The Place. That's the youth club the kids have fixed up in the basement here. The couple that's coming in this evening, they aren't much more than kids themselves. I sometimes think I'd rather perform a funeral service than a marriage. I feel it's probably a more useful service. I don't know about premarital counselling. I like to think it does some good. I try to bring them down to reality. I don't know much about this couple. So I'll start by asking them about themselves. When they met. What made them decide to get married. Then I'll say—I'll tell them that current statistics show that forty-five per cent of all new marriages end in divorce. And of those that don't, about half are more or less unhappy. I want them to realize that the odds are against a happy marriage. I want them to understand that marriage is a tough business. It's hard work. I tell them about the problems that can cause the most trouble. Money is probably No. 1. Then sex. Then communication. If they can't really communicate with each other, they don't have much chance of solving any of their problems. But if they're serious about it, and willing and able to work at it, marriage is the most exciting experience in life. The trouble is that most of them aren't serious. I had a couple in here about a year ago. He was eighteen and she was seventeen. I asked the girl the usual questions about why. Oh, well, she said, you know, she wanted to get away from home. There were too many people there, she said, and also when they were married she'd have a car to drive and more money to spend—all that. The boy had some kind of a part-time job. And he was going into the service in the fall. I did my best to get them to put it off, but . . ."

Collen—Robert Collen, the vice-president in charge of personnel at Rodney Hunt—sat down at his desk and lighted his pipe. The rest of us dropped into a scatter of Danish teak chairs. We were David Brown, vice-president in charge of engineering, and Hougen and I. Collen was a big man of forty-four with light wavy hair. Brown was big and dark and in his late thirties. They had given Hougen and me a two-hour tour of the plant. They had led us (equipped with safety glasses) through half a mile of shops, mills, and foundries, and now we were back in the carpeted quiet and the white walls—hung with posters by Ben Shahn and Bernard Buffet—of the administrative wing.

"Well, I enjoyed it, too," Collen said. "I seem to spend most of my time up at this end of the plant. But I wanted you to see our operation, Ed. I want us to know each other. We're the oldest industry in town, you know, and except for the paper mill I guess we're the biggest. And except for Dave we're all of us Congregationalists. Nominally, anyway."

"I know," Hougen said. "And I'm sorry about that. Everybody tells me how active you used to be."

"The only active religion around here these days is astrology," Brown said.

"I haven't turned away from religion," Collen said. "Only from the church. What I want is what everybody wants—something to help me integrate illness and death and all our other troubles with a view of life. With my life. Something that can relate my day-to-day concerns to some transcendental meaning. But I can't find it in the church."

"Why not?" Hougen said. "What turns you off? Is it the people? Or the boring sermons?"

"I've never heard you preach, Ed," Brown said. "I don't know anything about your sermons. But I do know there's something wrong when a minister begins to sound like Huntley and Brinkley or like William Buckley. There's a difference between affirming values and determining means to achieve social or political or economic ends."

"I think about theology a bit," Collen said. "But I find I don't think about the church anymore. I don't seem to need it. I can think without it and I can pray without it."

"I think the question is this," Brown said. "Do you want to be the most acceptable social club in town? Or do you want to be a link between a body of theology and the active intellectual potential of the community? Is it club or gospel?"

"Where does the church put its energy, Ed?" Collen said.

"The Sunday-morning service," Hougen said. "The Sunday-morning service has always been its focus."

"I agree," Collen said. "The fundamental mandate of the church is carrying the Good News."

"But doesn't that have any meaning for you anymore?" Hougen said. "Well, what needs of yours *could* the church meet?"

"I accept your question," Brown said. "But I can't answer it."

"I won't answer it," Collen said. "It's an uncongenial question."

"Well, there you are," Hougen said. He shrugged and looked glum. We were back in his little Simca. "You can see we've got our problems. And they're problems that every minister has to try to work out for himself. The answers aren't supplied at seminary. Not at Union Theological Seminary, where I went, anyway. About all I got out of Union Seminary was a wife. That's where Margaret and I met. But I have to agree with Bob Collen about carrying the Good News. Secular activities aren't all there is to Christianity. But that's where the kids are. And social events are where the adults are. Those are the things that really draw people to church. We can't just say, 'Come to us and be welcome.' We have to find out their interests and relate them to our program. One thing we're working on now is a tutoring project for the retarded at Belchertown State School. A lot of the teen-agers are interested in helping handicapped people, and I think our approach is working. I remember a girl in my first parish—an agnostic girl. She was interested only in social problems. That's what brought her to us. But then the church began to interest her. She got to reading about religion—all religion. Then she went off to college, and the last I heard she had had a conversion experience. That was great. I was very happy to hear it. But that isn't what I'm working for—or even hoping for. A conversion experience isn't the only way to faith. Belief is enough. Margaret is a believing Christian. Her faith is every bit as strong as mine, but she's never had a conversion experience. And it isn't that important. I think the church has a social responsibility to the community. It has to be part of the life of its time and place. Its basic responsibility, though, has never really changed. It's still leading people to the basic security and freedom of the Christian faith."

Hougen had two parish calls on his calendar for that night, and we met at the parsonage at seven o'clock. He was wearing his madras jacket and an orange turtleneck jersey. We drove down through the darkening tunnel of maples to the traffic signal and turned up West Main Street. There was the usual nightly gathering of sullen boys and girls sitting and squatting and roaming around the intersection. We climbed a hilly side street and stopped at a small white house with a towering television antenna. This was the home of a mill hand at the Erving Paper Mill named Claude Stack. A dark-haired young woman in cut-off bluejeans came to the door.

"Oh," she said. "Hi. Come in." We followed her into the living room. "Hey, Mom. Dad. It's Reverend Hougen."

Stack, a small, red-faced man of about fifty, was sitting on a sofa with a cigarette in his mouth and an ashtray full of butts at his elbow. Mrs. Stack sat huddled in a chair with a blanket over her knees and her right arm resting on a pillow on her lap. She was thin and gray and drawn.

"You'll have to excuse me, Reverend," she said. "I can't offer you my hand. I'm in therapy now, but my arm's still paralyzed, you know."

"I guess you know Mom had a fall," the young woman said.

Stack nodded a confirmation. He put out his cigarette and lighted another. "She fell out of bed," he said. "Three months ago."

"It was my second fall," Mrs. Stack said. "The first time was a concussion. But I took a ride this afternoon. Judy took me out for a drive. It was so good to get out again. I miss being able to jump in the car and go downstreet."

"I know," Hougen said. "And I'm glad to know you're feeling better. How have you been, Judy?"

"Well," she said, "did you see the paper today, Reverend? They printed my divorce. Thank God that's over. You know what the grounds were—gross and constant intoxication. He was drunk every day of our life together."

"It's a sickness," Mrs. Stack said.

"Sickness," Stack said. "Thank the good Lord for Blue Cross."

"Poor Dad," Mrs. Stack said. "It isn't only Judy and me. But Dad had his vacation last week, and that was the week the television broke down."

Mrs. Istel came out on the terrace with a tray of bottled beer and glasses. She was a tall, poised, attractive woman of around forty. Hougen and I helped ourselves to a glass and a bottle each, and Mrs. Istel sat down with her glass on a little settee. It was just dusk. We looked out in the fading light across a sloping meadow with a pond at one end to the trees and treetops massed below. Orange was somewhere below and beyond the trees.

"Right," Hougen said. "I hate sights—you know, scenery. It really turns me off. But I guess this is a terrific view."

"I've lived here since 1959," Mrs. Istel said. "Since before and after my divorce. But I've just found out why they call this Walnut Hill. Because all these trees are walnut trees."

"I don't know one tree from another," Hougen said.

"I suppose I'd been too busy to learn about things like that," she said. "I went on the Town Planning Board right after my divorce. And then they put me on the School Board. And, of course, I was teaching Sunday school. It all helped me to adjust to the divorce. But I've always been interested and involved in the church."

"Yes," Hougen said. "I know."

"I'll bet you don't," she said. "Not really. You knew that my brother is a Congregational minister? All right. But I'm not only the sister of a Congregational minister. I'm also the daughter of one, and a cousin of one, and a niece of one. All of them down in Connecticut."

"Wow," Hougen said.

"When I was growing up," she said, "I thought everybody's family was like that."

"I guess I really came to the right place," Hougen said. "Maybe you've got some thoughts about the church. Maybe you've got some ideas about what ought to be happening there."

"Well, there's certainly one thing," she said. "I like the way the church has moved in recent years. It's so much less stodgy. I like the social work it's doing. Community work, I mean. I've never cared for group social activities—the fun things. That's never been my kind of thing. I feel a little guilty about feeling that way. I suppose that's why I feel the way I do about women's lib. I'm content within my own skin. I think men and women are both playing roles that belittle them—that are forced upon them. Besides, equal pay and day-care centers are hardly something new. But no matter. My daughter Claudia loved the dances and dropping in at The Place and all that. I like very much what you're doing."

Hougen smiled a happy smile. He took a swallow of beer. "You know," he said, "there's a rumor all over town that you're going to have Margaret and me up here to dinner very soon."

"Oh," Mrs. Istel said. "You heard that, did you? I hoped you would."


We could hear the music a block away from the Armory. There were four of us—a couple named Bittenbender, Hougen, and I. Bittenbender, a young man with a black beard, was pastor of the Bethany Lutheran Church in Orange. We parked the car and crossed the street through the creeping traffic and climbed the Armory steps and into the shriek of rock. The music was that of a band called Spirit in Flesh, from the Brotherhood of the Spirit Commune, in Warwick, about ten miles north of town, and the concert was a benefit sponsored by the United Youth Ministry of Orange. The Bittenbenders were here as chaperones, but Hougen was merely making an expected appearance. There were several older couples gathered on the stoop outside the door. They were also chaperones, and they nodded to us and grimaced and held their ears.

The Bittenbenders stopped on the stoop, but Hougen and I went on through the doors and through the foyer (where a young man selling tickets at a table waved to Hougen and mouthed some affirma-

tive message) and into the scream and blast of the drill hall and a
transfixed crowd of three or four hundred teen-agers. We stopped
at the edge of the crowd, and got a good look at Spirit in Flesh
spread out across the stage: a drummer, an organist, three guitarists,
and a singer in a dirty white tank top writhing on the floor. It was
relentless hard rock, and I stood for a while and endured it. And
then it was too much. It began to hurt. I looked for Hougen, but
he was gone. I went back to the foyer and found him talking to a
pretty girl in glasses and a short, flowered dress. He beckoned me
over. He leaned close to the girl and said something in a shout.
Then he turned to me and put his mouth at my ear: "Let's go—
let's get out of here."

We sat in a booth in the House of Pizza ("Positively No Bare
Feet"), a hole in the wall on East Main Street. We had left the
Armory twenty minutes or more before, but my ears were still hum-
ming. Hougen made a doodle of moisture rings on the tabletop with
his Coke. "Oh, we'll make some money," he said. "It looked like a
pretty good crowd. Although, of course, they weren't all paying customers. A lot of them—the older ones—were from the commune,
and they all got in free. That girl I was talking to—she's a commune
girl. She was interesting. She told me she was a graduate nurse. She
said she made two day-long visits to the commune about a year ago,
and was so impressed by the spirit of love and openness and community. She said it answered something in her and she wanted to become
a part of it. It's a good commune, I understand. It's been going for
about four years, and they've got some strict rules. No drugs. No
sexual promiscuity. None of that kind of fun. So it isn't pleasure
that attracts them. It's something more satisfying, something much
more fundamental. It's tied up to the lack of continuity in life today—
people on the move, everything breaking up. That puts too much
pressure on the family to supply the community needs for belonging,
for love and affection. The family can't supply it all. It never could
and never will. But what bothers me is this: The need for belonging
to a community of people who care—people should find all that in
the church. That's what the church *is*. It *is* a community of people
who care. But the trouble is, we've got away from that. We offer
the trappings of community without providing the real thing, the

real openness. We don't really invite people to be themselves, and accept them for what they are. Over the generations, the church has become the most shockable community in the world—and it should be the least shockable. It should lay the least obligation on people to conform. But it has hardened into a kind of institution."

Hougen looked down at his glass. It was empty, and he pushed it away. "That's what we want to change," he said. "And we can. We have every opportunity. The individual minister in our church is really very free. He can move in any direction. He can define his job as he sees it. And I see mine—I see it pretty clearly. I see the church as a missionary force—to liberate and bring joy, to tell the Good News. And I see it as a sustaining force to renew and refresh the missionary. Christian faith is Christian action. I think faith exists only in action. There can't be a passive awareness of God. I believe that Christian life is a positive experience. And I believe the same of death."

"You believe in a life after death?" I said.

"Well, of course," he said. "That's fundamental to the Christian faith. If you eliminate that, there's nothing left of Christian theology but words. There's no community, no freedom, no love. I believe that something personal survives the phenomenon of death. Some essence of oneself. I believe that the 'I' that I am is preserved. And I'm not talking about atoms or recycling. I'll put it in old-fashioned language. I believe that everybody is going to Heaven." He smiled. "Ultimately, anyway."

# Solo

The Jal General Hospital stands on a little rise of gravelly ground just west of the town of Jal, in the rich Permian Basin oil fields of southeastern New Mexico. It was built as a unit of the Lea County hospital system in 1961; it has fifteen double rooms, an emergency room, and two operating rooms; and it serves a community of almost forty-five hundred people. The hospital staff consists of one full-time registered nurse, two part-time registered nurses, seven full-time licensed vocational nurses, three part-time licensed vocational nurses, two nurse's aides, an office manager, two secretaries, a dietary supervisor and four kitchen workers, a janitor, a housekeeper, a laboratory and X-ray technician, and a physician. The physician, whom I recently got to know, is a general practitioner of forty named Elwood L. Schmidt, and he is the only doctor in town.

I came to Jal from Texas—West Texas. I drove from the airport at Midland through Odessa and Notrees and Kermit in a rented car with the radio shouting Pentecostal hymns: "I will never let the Devil win/I will never compromise with sin." Kermit is fifty miles from Odessa, and Jal is eighteen miles (and just across the Texas-New Mexico line) from Kermit, and it was desert all the way. It was flat red sand and gray gravel, mesquite and bunchgrass and tumbleweed, and there were oil wells everywhere. Most of the wells were pumping, and often in the distance there was a silver skyline cluster of bulk-storage tanks and fractionating towers. Along the road were red warning signs: "Caution: Low Pressure Gas Line," "Caution: High Pressure Oil Pipe Line," "Caution: Telephone Cable Underground." There was always a circling hawk in the high blue sky overhead, and the driver of every car I passed raised a finger from the wheel in greeting. I spent the night at the Circle A Motel, on the eastern outskirts of Jal (where I learned from a Chamber of Commerce brochure that the town took its curious name from the cattle brand of an early settler named J. A. Lynch), and ate an early breakfast with a crowd of hardhat roustabouts at a highway café called Theresa's, and then drove out to the hospital to meet Dr. Schmidt in time for his morning rounds.

The hospital is a long, low building, built of cement blocks painted the color of adobe, with a dusty planting of yuccas out front. I left my car in the parking lot and went into the waiting room. There was a row of chairs along one wall, and across from them were a bench and a little table piled with tattered magazines. On the bench lay a gray-haired man in work clothes and stocking feet. He was asleep and snoring, and he smelled of beer. Through a doorway at the end of the room was a long corridor lined with closed doors: "Emergency Room," "Men," "Janitor," "No Smoking." The "No Smoking" door opened, and Dr. Schmidt emerged—a big man with short, light hair, a long, flat nose, and a wide, smiling mouth. His trousers were green, his jacket was a green-and-brown check, his shirt was yellow, and he wore a yellow-and-brown striped tie. Behind him came a young nurse in a white uniform.

"This is Edna Jean Featherston," he said. "Edna Jean is one of our L.V.N.s, and she is also my rounds nurse this morning." He looked down at the man on the bench. "This poor fellow lost his wife a couple of years back. She died here at the hospital. Sometimes, when he has a few too many, he comes up here to sleep it off. Memories, I suppose. Well, I've got some patients to see. Let's get going."

The rounds cart was waiting down the corridor, in front of the nursing station. It was a metal teacart spread with medical supplies and equipment. Eight patients' charts in metal binders hung on a rack at one end. Dr. Schmidt took a swallow of coffee from a mug on the cart and hung a stethoscope around his neck. Mrs. Featherston got behind the cart, and we followed him down the hall—past a painting of an oil well with cacti and mountains in the background, past "Nursery," past "Laboratory"—to an unmarked door on the left. He took a chart from the rack *(Bruce Marts, 45. Turbine operator, El Paso Natural Gas Co. Duodenal ulcer)* and opened the door.

"How do you feel, Bruce?"

"I feel good. I feel like a fiddle."

"Have you stopped smoking?"

"Well . . ."

"All right. If I send you home with some tablets, can you function?"

"You mean can I work? I think so. I'm ready to try."

"All right. Now hear this. Cigarette smoking is *not* good for your ulcer. This is accepted by medicine as a *fact*. So *don't*. Whatever the temptation. Or provocation. Whatever happens on the job. Whatever somebody says to you. Or whatever they don't say. I know what I'm asking—I haven't had a cigarette in my mouth for sixteen months three weeks and four days, but I still remember the pleasure. I remember, but I don't smoke. And I don't have an ulcer. So."

"Well—I'll keep trying."

"I'll see you at my office in, let's say, two months."

"All right. But, you know, I've been laying here thinking. I mean, all that terrible pain, and you say this ulcer wasn't no bigger than the end of a matchstick."


*Robert Snider, 27. Machine operator, Trans-West Pipeline Maintenance Co. Upper respiratory infection.*

"I didn't hear you hacking as I came down the hall. You must be getting better."

"I been coughing."

"Let's take a look at your ears. Well, that looks better. Now let's see your throat. Uh-huh. And your chest sounds pretty nice. How about your belly?"

"Well, it don't really ache. It just feels sour down there."

"You've got a good X-ray. No ulcer. And the signs are good. But I think we'll check your stomach acids. It's no problem unless you gag easily. It's just a matter of putting a tube down your throat."

"Whatever you say. But I sure don't feel like going home. I still feel sour."

*Jack McKeown, 68. Cotton farmer. Observation.*

"Well, Jack, you're looking a lot better than you did when they dragged you in last night."

"I feel a lot better."

"Let me hear your heart. Bang, bang, bang—real good. Real strong. Now give me your arm. I want to check your blood pressure. Mmm. O.K. No problem there. And the electrocardiogram we took last night was fine. I think we'll take another—just to be sure. But now I want to know a little more about what happened. You weren't doing a whole lot of talking last night. All I know is you were sitting in the pool hall and all of a sudden—what? You passed out?"

"I don't rightly know. I was setting there watching some fellows playing dominoes, and I come on gradually sick. I felt dizzy, like I was drunk. But I hadn't had a drink of anything all day. Not even a Coke. I hadn't even eaten anything since breakfast. I drove up to Lubbock, where I got a farm, and I started to work breaking land and I guess I just forgot about dinner. Then I come back home and stopped at the pool hall, and that was when it happened. The next think I knew was some fellows were shaking me and I was wet with sweat and I must have been asleep."

"Jack, I think you're crazy. I think you're a plain damn fool. You drove—how far is it to your place?"

"It's a hundred and ten miles, about."

"You drove a hundred and ten miles up and a hundred and ten miles back, and plowed I don't know how many acres of land, and didn't eat any dinner or even drink a Coke, and you're sixty-eight years old. There may be something serious here, and I'm sure going to find out, but I doubt it. My guess is you just plain wore yourself out."

"Well, I'm resting now."


*Johnny Mack Owen II, 9. Father, office clerk, El Paso Natural Gas Co. Possible duodenal ulcer.*

"Good morning, Johnny Mack. What's that you're reading?"

"It isn't reading. It's a crossword puzzle."

"How's your belly?"

"It feels O.K."

"Let's see what it sounds like. Mmm. It's growling pretty good."

"Did you get the X-rays done?"

"I did. And they don't show an ulcer. They don't show what we call a crater. That's like a little hole. But I don't think that means you haven't got an ulcer. It's like when you're out hunting and you find some deer tracks in the snow. Then you see some deer droppings. Then you come to a tree where a deer has rubbed his horns. Well, you haven't seen an actual deer, but you know there's one around. You *presume* he's there. It's the same with you. We don't see an ulcer, but we can presume from various signs that it's probably there."

"Oh. I'd like to go deer hunting in the mountains sometime."

"I'm sure you will."

"What's a 'mimic'?"

"What? Oh, you mean for your puzzle. It means to make like. To imitate."

"Like a monkey?"

"Right. I'll see you tonight."

*Laura Lee Whipple, 31. Husband, welder, Jal Welding & Machine Works. Vomiting.*

"I don't know. I guess I'm some better."

"No more nausea?"

"Not really. And I did eat some breakfast."

"Good. And you didn't have any nausea yesterday. Well, why don't I let you go home? I guess I will. Now—what to do at home. Frequent small meals. I won't try to tell you that this is the end of it. That would be a story. But the end will come—it's bound to come when the baby is born. You know that from the last time."

"I don't know why I feel this way, Doctor. I didn't feel like this when I was carrying my first baby. I felt real happy. And the second one, too. It seemed to begin with the third. And now—you know, I think this is the worst of all."

"Yes. Well. And now—when you see your friends, what are you going to say? Do you have to say, 'I've been in the hospital for three days because I'm pregnant again and I can't keep a thing on my stomach'? No, you don't. Tell them this: 'I had a touch of hyper-emesis gravidarum.' "

"What in the world does that mean?"

"It means 'I'm pregnant and I can't keep a thing on my stomach.' "

*Joe Don Evans, 31. Radio operator, El Paso Natural Gas Co. Bronchitis.*

"Joe Don here is one of my showpieces. Am I right, Edna Jean? He's one of the very few patients I've ever done a tonsillectomy on. I don't believe in routine tonsillectomies. I think it's a pernicious operation. Most doctors feel the same. It's the public that believes in tonsillectomies. They want to have the children's tonsils out because it's a tradition. It's American. But Joe Don was a different case. His tonsils were a mess. They had to come out. How are you this morning?"

"I'm not as miserable as I was."

"Your chest sounds good. Is it hurting any?"

"I don't hurt anywhere."

"Maybe we can get you out of here by Sunday. The only thing your tests still show is a little white-blood-cell elevation."

"Let's make it Saturday."

"Saturday? You got a big night planned?"

"You know about Saturday—it's Hal Baker's barbecue. Aren't you and Fay going?"

"What's he barbecuing?"

"Goat, man. You tell him, Edna Jean. San Angelo goat. Hal and them were out getting mesquite for the fire last week."

"Well, then. I guess you might be there. I'll think about it, anyway."

*Lavinia Tredway, 52. Husband, house painter & roustabout. Acute bronchitis & anxiety state.*

"They tell me you're still coughing."

"Not too much."

"And you're still on those damn cigarettes."

"I've been trying not to."

"Well, keep trying. It's your only hope. Now breathe for me. I want to listen to your chest. You sound better—and you look a little bit better. What does your husband say?"

"He come in here last night thinking to be nice by visiting me. He'd changed his clothes and everything. I guess it was for me. But I don't know. It wasn't too good. We got a little nervous."

"Was he—"

"I don't believe he'd had a single drink. You know, Doctor, I just don't understand this drinking. I don't mean him. I mean me. I don't ever really want a drink. I mean, why do I take that first drink? That sure isn't my idea of a good time. People say there's nothing to do around here but drink. But I know people that don't drink. Maybe I ought to play cards. Or go to the cockfights. I wish they had a movie. I like to cook a good dinner. But something always seems to happen. You know that burn on my elbow—where I leaned on a cigarette? I didn't even feel it."

"How much were you smoking then? How many packs a day?"

"Three, I guess. No, I'll be honest—it was more like four."

"Well, you've made some progress. And you're pretty well dried out."

"I don't even like the taste of *beer.*"


*William Harris, 28. Electrician, El Paso Natural Gas Co. Back pain.*

"Good news, Bill. The X-rays of your back are all right. Nothing showed. How do you feel?"

"I feel better. I feel real good."

"Those are sweet words to a doctor. You mean, no pain at all?"

"Not really. You know, I wish I knew how this happened. That motor I was lifting, it didn't weigh much more than a hundred and fifty pounds, and I can lift that easy. Heck, I'm a weight lifter, you know that. I guess what I did was pick it up a little twisted."

"I'll bet you dropped it real fast."

"Oh, I didn't drop it. It hurt like heck, but I carried it on over to the pump. Shoot, you can't just drop a valuable electric motor like that."

"Swing your feet over the side of the bed and let's look at your reflexes. Good—that's good. I think you are a whole lot better. Now let's see you stand up. Now walk over to the door and back. That's right—keep walking. Yesh, offisher, I can walk that there line as straight as anybody. Very good. Now, I'm going to give you some exercises. You know them. You learned them in the service. They'll give you something to do when you're tired of reading—what's that magazine there? . . . Oh? Well, now. I didn't know you were a drag racer, Bill."

"Oh, sure."

"Bill, I will say you're much farther along than I expected. But I have to say this. There's always a chance that you'll cough and *bang*— a setback. I'm telling you so you won't worry if it happens. It's not at all uncommon with a back like yours."

"What do you call a back like mine?"

"I don't know. There isn't a name for everything. It don't have to have a name to hurt, and it don't have to have a name to be treated. I know folks like to have things named. But I can't always oblige."

"Well, I'll try not to cough."

Harris was the end of morning rounds. I looked at my watch: it was nine-twenty. We went back up the long hall. Johnny Mack Owen's door was open. He was sitting up in bed with the television on, a model airplane in his lap, and a book in his hand: "The Mystery of the Mountain Cave." We left Mrs. Featherston and the cart at the nursing station, and the duty nurse handed Dr. Schmidt a handful of memoranda. He stuffed them in his pocket. The sleeper was gone from the waiting room. Outside, there was a pale-blue Mercury sedan parked at a "Doctors Only" sign.

"Have you got a car?" Dr. Schmidt said. "Well, leave it here and ride back to my office with me. You can pick it up later. We'll be coming back here again. And, probably, again. Well, that was nice and quiet, wasn't it? No crises. Although I must say I've been a little bit worried about Bruce Marts and that ulcer of his. I mean, this isn't his first one."

"You seem to see a lot of ulcers."

"Right. There *are* a lot of ulcers. Johnny Mack's dad has one, and so does his mother. I don't know why. I wish I did. Except that most of the plants here work their people on rotating shifts— tours, they call them. That can play hell with the human body. I never take any chances with an ulcer. They frighten me. I have an old fellow in the hospital at Kermit who has me scared to death. I was conditioned on ulcers by a teacher at medical school. I'm from South Texas, and I studied at the University of Texas Medical Branch, at Galveston. I graduated in 1956. That's where I met my wife. Ila Fay is a Texan, too, from Amarillo, and she's also an R.N. She worked until the children began to come along. Well, that teacher taught me that an untreated ulcer was a cocked pistol. When something suggests an ulcer to me, I want that man in the hospital. Of course, hospitalization isn't the problem here that it is in so many places. We usually have a bed, and the expense doesn't matter too much. Our big industry in Jal is El Paso Natural Gas. They've got four big plants and their Permian Division offices here. I understand there are pipelines under practically every inch of Lea County. Anyway, El Paso has a very liberal health-insurance program. They take good care of their people. El Paso built my office in order to get a doctor here. Not me—my predecessor, Dr. O'Loughlin. And they charge me a very nominal rent. Dr. O'Loughlin left soon after I arrived, in 1961. He's practicing in Abilene now. I wish he had stayed here. I wish I had *some* help. You know, it's almost funny. I came here because Dr. O'Loughlin needed help. I was practicing in Slaton, Texas, up near Lubbock, and Slaton was over-doctored. It was full of doctors, and I had so little to do I was bored to death, and when the Jal Chamber of Commerce advertised for another doctor I jumped at the chance. And now look at me! I haven't had a day off in four months. Solo practice has its satisfactions, but this is just a little too solo. My God, when my wife and I want to be alone for a little while at night I've got to take the telephone off the hook."

We turned off the highway and drove down a long, bare block of little brick houses set in little bare yards. We passed a new brick post office on a lawn with a flagpole. We turned into Main Street, a wide business street with a concrete mall down the middle and two blocks of one-story buildings—Wacker's Variety Store, City Barber Shop, Jal Recreation Center, Aunt Dorothy's Cafe, Roy & Rena's Bar, Midget Cafe, Bob's Superette, Cactus Bar, New Mexico Bank & Trust Co., Bert's Place, Lewis Drugs, Jal Cleaners, McKeown's Dry Goods. We turned off Main Street and pulled up at a one-story cement-block building painted pale blue. It was planted with evergreens, and there was an inscription above the door: "Jal Medical Center."

"We'll go in the back way," Dr. Schmidt said. "The waiting room is just a waiting room, and it's probably full of folks. I see patients from when I get here in the morning until they let me leave for lunch, and from when I get back until they stop coming. Everything opens off this hall. That door on the left is our X-ray room, and this one here is the laboratory. My girls do simple X-rays and routine laboratory tests. I like to have a white blood count when somebody's got a cough or such. These four numbered doors are consultation rooms. The girls bring the patients in and get their histories and get them ready, and I see them in turn. My private office is here on the right, and this is the general office. I want you to meet Mary Butler. Mary is my receptionist and bookkeeper. And these lovely girls are the nurses. They work for me, and their husbands all work for El Paso. Cecilia Davis. Joan Roberts. Nadine Brookings. All right, girls. Quick—while I've got a chance—some coffee. And what are you all grinning about?"

"Here's a present for you, Doctor," Mrs. Davis said.

"Oh? Hey—chocolate-chip cookies. And homemade. Where did they come from?"

"Dana Riggs brought them in on her way to school."

"Well, now. Wasn't that nice!"

"What I want to know is this," Mrs. Butler said. "Why are you getting presents from a pretty girl like Dana?"

"I let her correct my grammar when she was in here yesterday," Dr. Schmidt said. "I let her think she knew the difference between 'shall' and 'will.' "

We drank our coffee (sweetened with saccharin and stirred with a wooden tongue depressor) in Dr. Schmidt's office. The office was hung with framed diplomas and certificates—from the University of Texas at Galveston; from White Cross Hospital, in Columbus, Ohio (where he interned); from the American Academy of General Practice—and his desk was piled with books and papers and periodicals, and decorated with two standing photographs. One was a studio triptych of his children (three small boys), and the other was a grinning chimpanzee in a doctor's white coat, with the caption "Whatever it was you had, you've got it again." Dr. Schmidt sipped his coffee and looked at his mail and ate a chocolate-chip cookie. The telephone

rang, and he answered it ("Oh? No—that's not too good. . . . Yes,
I do. . . . I'll turn you back to Nadine. She'll give you an appointment") and wrote something on a memorandum pad and ate another
cookie. There was a knock at the door, and Mrs. Roberts looked
in. Dr. Schmidt nodded, and drank the last of his coffee and stood
up. We went out and across the hall to a numbered door with a
folder clipped to the panel. He took down the folder and gave it a
glance *(Mrs. Burma Cusenbary, 33. Husband, electrician, El Paso
Natural Gas Co. Pain)* and opened the door.

"You, too? That husband of yours was in here just the other day
about cutting his finger half off. What's *your* trouble?"

"You're going to laugh at me. But my jaw hurts. It hurts when I
chew. It's like there's something wrong with my wisdom teeth. Only
I don't have any wisdom teeth anymore."

"Very good. Your description is excellent. There's a six-hundred-
page book devoted to the joint where the jaw hooks onto the skull,
and it doesn't say it any better than you did. They call it the temporo-
mandibular joint. Has it ever locked on you?"

"Oh, yes. That's what is so embarrassing. Sometimes when I'm
laughing. I can't close it—I have to take my hands and *push* it shut."

"Well, you can get arthritis there like anywhere else. The question
is, what do we do?"

"I suppose you could amputate my jaw."

"That may not be necessary. Let's try aspirin first. Let's say eight
or ten tablets every day, and take them at mealtime. I think that
may be all you need. If not, we'll start thinking about a dentist.
How's Phil doing?"

"He's fine. But he was lucky, wasn't he?"

"He could have lost the end of his finger, you mean? Yes, he
was lucky."


*Cavin Horne, 5. Father, rig operator, El Paso Natural Gas Co. Cough.*

"Good morning, Mrs. Horne. Good morning, Cavin. So your mother
is making you play hooky from kindergarten."

"I didn't want to take any chances, Doctor. He was coughing
again, and he had a fever of 101.2 last night."

"Mmm. I don't hear any wheezing. I don't find any evidence of
pneumonia. I think he's just back on his old bronchitis. You're a

pretty experienced patient, aren't you, Cavin? We've got a real big history on you for a boy of five—including a duodenal ulcer. But we'll lick 'em yet."

"I wonder, Doctor. His sister, you know, she went through a period like this, with a regular cough and a runny nose, but she finally outgrew it. Do you think maybe Cavin will do the same?"

"Could be, I guess. But you're right about kindergarten. I'm afraid Cavin will be playing hooky all the rest of the week."

"Did I tell you we're moving? I think where we're going there may be less dust. I hope so—for all our allergies. What do you think?"

"I think it's dusty everywhere."


*Benjamin May, 21. Production dispatcher, El Paso Natural Gas Co. Knee.*

"That's an ugly-looking knee. What did you do to it?"

"It's a floor burn. I got it playing basketball out at the plant. Then it like got infected."

"So I see. Now I'll tell you what you're going to do. One: get some soap and work up a thick lather on your knee. Two: rub this ointment on it. Three: here are some penicillin tablets. That's for the infection, in case it's strep. I could do a ten-dollar laboratory analysis and wait five days for the results to come back, but I'm going to save you time and money and assume it's strep."

"O.K."

"Now, wait a minute. That isn't all. I'm going to give you a free lecture. The subject is that red stuff you painted on your knee— whatever it is. That's what caused all this trouble. I know this goes against your lifelong American sports tradition, but never, *never,* NEVER put that red stuff on a wound. It burns it. It irritates it. It's *no good* on broken skin. And try to keep from falling down for the next five days."


*Cynthia Wood, 8. Father, head of W. E. Gray Roustabout Service. Rash.*

"Doctor, I want you to look at this child. I don't know what you're going to say, but I got to thinking and worrying. Her first bumps come out about a week ago. Now those on her back look like they're getting well. The ones on her stomach there, they're the newest ones. Now, what comes to my mind was the chicken pox."

"Oh?"

"That's right. That's exactly what I got to thinking."

"Well, let's take a look. I'm looking at your stomach, Cynthia. And now I'm pinching something between my fingers. What do you think it's called?"

"Fat?"

"Right. And what do you think you ought to do about it?"

"Diet?"

"Right. You don't want to be a big fat girl that can't play and have any fun. Now, about this rash. I don't think it's chicken pox. I don't think it's an allergy, like hives. I think these are some kind of bug bites. Do you-all have a dog?"

"A dog? We got a hound."

"Good. I suggest you go on home and look him over for fleas. Meanwhile, I'll give Cynthia some oral antihistamine for the itching. And let me know about the dog."

*Jack Leisure, 46. Jal Water Dept. Ulcer.*

"This is just a checkup, isn't it, Jack?"

"That's right. I'm doing real good. I think that ulcer is all healed up."

"I think so, too. I think it started healing the minute you sold your filling station and went back to work for the city."

"I know it did. I shouldn't never have tried it on my own. It don't make me happy to be the boss. I'd rather somebody else had the worries."

"You had a sad experience. But I guess it was instructive."

"I learned a lot. I learned that when you give your friends credit and they don't pay, you lose your money and you lose your friends, both."

*Mrs. Sandra Phillips, 22. Husband, welder. Pregnant.*

"I don't know what I'm going to do with you."

"I'm too heavy, ain't I?"

"You're much too heavy. Do you know what you weigh? Two

hundred and three pounds. Now, listen to me. Excessive weight gain in the first pregnancy is associated with a lot of troubles. It's courting disaster. I mean, it's dangerous. Your blood pressure is borderline high. Good nutrition is important for you and the baby, but too much is too much."

"My husband, he don't help me."

"What do you mean?"

"I try to cut down on eating and he gets mad. He goes on like crazy. He says I'm starving the baby."

"Well, I say you aren't. You tell him to stop practicing medicine. I don't tell him how to weld."

*Mrs. Barbara Stirman, 57. Husband, pipe fitter. Gallstones.*

"You're looking pretty good, Mrs. Stirman. I hope you feel that way."

"I guess I do—at times. But that diet you gave me. It's a problem. Everything is so difficult here. I guess I'm spoiled. My husband had three solid years of work in one place before we came here. We even had a house. I don't know, I get so sick of travelling from job to job. You know, we've been in Alaska and up in Montana and in Wyoming and over to Oklahoma. It was nice having a house. But now we're back in a trailer, and it's crowded and it's cold and the windows are drafty. And the stores here. You can't buy anything bigger than a match except you go down to Kermit or Odessa. You can't get skim milk. You can't get dry cottage cheese. That's what I meant about your diet. And then last night I ate something that made me sick. I guess it was the spaghetti."

"Well, that wasn't real sensible, was it?"

"I guess not. But I get so blue. Living in a trailer and all."

"How are you sleeping?"

"Oh, I sleep all right. I never complain about sleeping. But did you ever hear of somebody having triple vision?"

"I've heard of everything. Do you have it?"

"Yes."

"When did it begin?"

"I was going down the hall of the trailer, and it hit me just like that. It was like that vent you've got up there on the wall—I see three of it. It's a crazy feeling."

"I'm sure it is. But I don't think we'll change anything. I think we'll stay with the prescriptions you have for another two weeks. Then call me."

"I don't even have a telephone in that trailer."


*Jennifer Hicks, 8 months. Father, pastor, Church of Christ Church. Cough.*

"Well, Mrs. Hicks, how are you liking Jal by now?"

"I like it fine—we both do."

"I forget where you come from."

"From Roby. I come from Roby, Texas. That's up near Abilene. But I didn't live right in town. I lived, oh my goodness, ten miles out of town. That's how I come to mislike towns. Jal is just about right for me—for us. I'm not so much on this fast pace of living."

"Well, I know what you mean. But what's the trouble with Jennifer?"

"I thought she sounded croupy. She sounded awful croupy yesterday. And this morning she woke up crying."

"Her white blood count is normal. But I'm just a little bit worried. I'm wondering if this is asthma. But I have to say no to that. You don't see asthma in a baby under two. Does that mean she's likely to develop asthma later on? Yes, it does. It's very possible. Is there anything to do? Probably not. But we're going to try diet—a milk-free diet. And a dust-free environment. And I'm going to prescribe an antihistamine. Then we'll see."

"You think she's going to get asthma?"

"It's possible. But we can take comfort in the old saying: All that wheezes is not asthma. Suppose you bring her back in about ten days."


*Mrs. Billie Beaird, 33. Husband, head of Jal Gas Co. Ear.*

"Tell me about your ear."

"Well, it started out just itching. Then it got kind of sore. Then it started roaring. It's this left one. And it bothers me."

"O.K. Now—open your mouth."

"You want to look in my mouth?"

"I thought I might."

"Then wait a sec. I got to get rid of my gum."

"I'll wait. All right? O.K. Now turn your head so I can look at your ears. Mmmm. And you can go back to your gum if you like."

"I swallowed it."

"Well, that's getting rid of it. About your ear. I think what you've got is a nervous rash. I'm going to give you some eardrops. *My God!* I'm prescribing eardrops. Well, there are times when they are indicated, and this is one of those times."

*Fernando Acosta, 28. Jal Water Dept. Burn.*

"How in the name of God did you do it?"

"I spilled some sulphuric acid. I splashed some on my pants and—oh, Jesus, it burned right through to my leg. So quick. Then it began to hurt. I washed it off with soap and water, and somebody gave me this salve. Is it any good?"

"Only for the manufacturer. Give it to me. See that wastebasket over there? Now watch. Gone. I'll give you something that *will* help—an antibiotic ointment. But that damn stuff you had—it makes me mad. It makes me furious. Some damn fool congressman will stand up and raise Cain about the Pill. That gets his name in the paper. Why don't they speak out about these damn benzocaine preparations? They're promoted for topical anesthesia for burns and abrasions, and they help very little or none. They can actually be harmful. There are local reactions and systemic reactions and severe allergic reactions—all possible and all well reported. But I guess there's more goddamn political mileage in yelling about the Pill."

*Mrs. Eloise Dobbs, 38. Husband, feed store. Chest pain.*

"This whole side of my chest hurts, Elwood. It really hurts."

"What about your heart—any irregular beat?"

"I haven't noticed any. Elwood, I just want to feel good again."

"That's a reasonable request. And I think it's very possible you will."

"But what do you think? Is it my heart? Is it my lungs?"

"Now, you won't believe this—but I don't know. I do not know.

But I wonder. Are you lifting any sacks down at the store?"

"I lift some. But only fifty pounds or so. And only for the woman customers."

"I think you'd better let your lady customers lift their own sacks. If I know those ladies, they can do it just as well as you can. Maybe better."

*Lester Sharp, 62. Operator. Pain.*

"Well, Lester—what is it today?"

"I got trouble. That goddam pain."

"You mean your ulcer? Or your arthritis?"

"I mean my leg. That damn pain goes right down my leg. I called you the other day, but you were out."

"The girls said you called, but you didn't make an appointment."

"No, I didn't. I was in pain. I went to see a doctor in Kermit. But he didn't give me no satisfaction. None at all. Then I tried a chiropractor and—"

"All right, Lester. Don't tell me about your chiropractor, you hear? Or I'll get mad, real mad."

"I tell you this pain hasn't let me be in two whole weeks. Oh, damn, I need help."

"Then drop your pants and get up on the table. Is this the spot?"

"That and all around there."

"All right. I'm going to give you two injections. The first is a local anesthetic. Roll over on your belly and hold still. I said hold still. And this one is cortisone. I think—God damn it, Lester, hold still! You've got a three-inch needle sticking in your butt. How's your ulcer?"

"It's all right. It don't bother me much."

"Is that a fact? Well, I'm surprised. One of the girls saw you at the store the other day. She said you were buying a carton of cigarettes and a case of Coke."

"Ohhh. By God, I feel better already. I think you saved my life."

Dr. Schmidt and I had our lunch (or noon dinner) in Kermit. He had two Medicare patients in Memorial Hospital there whom he wished to see. Memorial, where Dr. Schmidt has staff privileges, is a large hospital with an intensive-care unit and other sophisticated facilities not available at Jal General. We stopped at the hospital first. One of the patients was an elderly woman in intensive care. The other was the man of whom he had spoken—an elderly man with a duodenal ulcer. ("Frank's been bleeding on and off all week," Dr. Schmidt said as we left the hospital. "I don't know how many pints of blood we've had to give him. He also has congestive heart failure and emphysema. But you noticed when we came into the room—there he was with a cigarette in his mouth.") Kermit is the seat of Winkler County, and we lunched (or dined) at a café on the courthouse square called Dolly's Family Style Meals. We shared a table for eight with five other men. Dr. Schmidt knew them all. The food was on the table, and we helped each other and ourselves. There was a platter of sliced pot roast and a bowl of chicken fricassee. There were yellow grits and mashed potatoes and giblet dressing and sweet potatoes with marshmallows. There were black-eyed peas and red beans and green beans and collard greens and carrots and broccoli and creamed corn and a gravy boat of pepper sauce. There was Waldorf salad and fruit salad and combination salad. There was corn bread and rolls and hot biscuits. There was a pound of butter on a plate and a bowl of grape jelly. There was iced tea and hot coffee. Dessert was peach cobbler. There was no tipping. We paid the cashier. There was a dish of after-dinner mints on the counter and a cup of toothpicks. Our lunches (or dinners) were a dollar and a half apiece.

"I don't eat like that every day," Dr. Schmidt said. "I usually go home for lunch. Although I will say Aunt Dorothy's Cafe in Jal has a real good meat loaf. When the weather is nice, I like to walk to lunch. It's about a mile from my office to home, and I need the exercise. Of course, it isn't easy. I can hardly walk a block without somebody driving by and stopping with something they want to ask me about. This is good country for walking. We don't have any hills, and it almost never rains. Our New Mexico weather is really pretty nice. They tell about a couple of old girls living up on the New Mexico-Colorado line in a strip of country that both states claimed. For a while, it was called New Mexico. Then Colorado took it over. Finally, the states agreed to submit the matter to arbitration, and the day the commission announced its decision one old girl came running home with the news: Their land was in New Mexico. The other old girl gave a sigh. 'Well, thank heavens,' she said. 'I tell you, Mary Flo, I just don't think I could have stood another of those Colorado winters.' I like that story. So true. And I like this kind of day. Not too cool. Very little wind. I suppose there are people somewhere out playing golf today. Dreams of bliss. Playing golf in the middle of the week. I've done it once or twice. I remember the last time. I was playing with a doctor friend in Kermit, and he mentioned a patient of his who was having a sleep problem. He was waking up very early and he couldn't get back to sleep. He lay there thinking. There were a couple of other things my doctor friend told me, and I said it sounded to me like a case of depression—endogenous depression. I said if the man were my patient I'd hospitalize him for some close observation. People like that have a high suicide potential. Just getting them into the hospital environment is sometimes a very big help. The home can be the enemy, you know. In that and a lot of other conditions. Anyway, I was eating supper that night when the phone rang, and it was my Kermit friend. He thought I would be interested to know that the fellow we were talking about that afternoon had just put a shotgun in his mouth and blown his head off."

It was almost two o'clock when we got back to the Medical Center in Jal. I counted five cars nosed in at the curb in front. One of them had a bumper sticker: "Why Not? Jal, N.M." The doors of all the consultation rooms were closed, and there were folders already clipped to the panels. Dr. Schmidt took off his checked jacket and sat down at his desk and looked at a long memorandum. The telephone rang.

"Yes," he said. "I was just looking at it. I'll see him on evening rounds. Thank you, Nadine. . . . What? . . . All right—put her on." He looked at me and made a long face. "Hello? . . . Yes? . . . Oh, no. . . . Oh, dear. . . . Oh, hell. . . . That's bad news. I guess we were a little too optimistic. Oh, yes—by all means. I'll have one of the girls make the arrangements. And don't you worry about anything. I'll see you tonight at the hospital." He hung up. "That was the pregnant lady we saw at the hospital this morning. Poor girl. As soon as she got home, she started in vomiting again. I wish all my cases were as easy to understand as that. It's all very

sad and simple. The only trouble is, I can't do a whole lot for her."
He pushed back his chair. "Well, let's see what's on the program
for this afternoon."


*Steven Brooks, 16. Father, operator. Ear.*

"Hello, Steve. My God—what did you do to your hair?"

"I guess I kind of let it grow."

"I guess you did—all the way. Well, what's this about your ear?"

"It's my right ear. It's just been, you know, ringing."

"Nobody fetched you like a clout on that ear?"

"Oh, no. But it seems like— You remember I had mononucleosis
a while back. It seems like I've been noticing this ringing since about
then."

"I guess there could be some connection. But that's pretty far-
fetched. Tell me more."

"Well, I wash my hair a lot. And then, of course, I've got this
little rock band. I play drums."

"Go on. You have my full attention."

"Well, I spend a lot of time, you know, practicing? I mean, I
set my drums between the speakers and turn them up pretty high.
You think that could be it?"

"I think I'll see how well you hear this tuning fork. Now, tell
me when you stop hearing the sound. . . . Yes? . . . O.K.? . . .
Now? . . . Still hearing it? . . . Mmm. Well, your ears are balanced,
and there's no hearing loss as far as I can tell from this. But amplified
music—any kind of amplified music—can result in definite hearing
loss. There have been a lot of studies on that subject lately. It's
like working in a boiler factory. I suggest you lay off practicing for
a few days. And before you play your next gig, get yourself a pair
of earplugs. They won't keep you from functioning, but they will
cut down the noise. That's all I can suggest right now—give your
ears a rest. If the ringing continues or gets worse, we'll think about
a specialist."

"O.K. Hey—I just thought of something, Doctor. I get some noise
at school, too. I take welding in shop."

"Get those earplugs."

*James Day, 4 weeks old, and Donald Day, 2. Father, pipe fitter, El Paso Natural Gas Co. Cough.*

"What's this—an epidemic?"

"It's really just Jamie, Doctor. Little old Jamie, he can't hardly breathe. The minute he lays flat, he starts snorting. Don here, he's just got himself a cough. Jamie started in coughing the night before last. He eats fine. It's just that he has a rough time breathing."

"Well, let's take a look. Mmm. Uh-huh. Well. What are you feeding him?"

"I just now started him on a little rice cereal."

"You did, eh? Very good. You did right. I give you an A in my record book. I like to see all my four-week-old babies started on rice cereal. O.K. Now, I'm going to give you some nose drops for Jamie. I think we can forget about Don. He's all right. But about the nose drops—let's don't overdo it. I don't like those things—you can get hooked on them. Have you got a vaporizer?"

"Have I got a vaporizer? In Jal, New Mexico? Is there anybody here who hasn't got one?"

"Probably not. But get yours out. And keep in touch. I sure want to know if Jamie starts running any kind of fever."


*Richard Muncrief, 12. Father, operator, El Paso Natural Gas Co. Backache.*

"Hello, Mrs. Muncrief. Hi, Rick. Now, who's got the nagging backache?"

"Well, for once it isn't me, Doctor. It's Rick."

"Where does it hurt, Rick?"

"Up here—up along the spine. It hurts worst when I first get up."

"How about when you urinate?"

"A little bit."

"O.K. Let's see if I can find anything. Lean to the right. Now to the left. Now back. Now toward your toes—way down. All right. How about joint pain?"

"No."

"Hip pain?"

"No."

"Here—kick my hand. Now the other foot."

"Rick isn't a complainer, Doctor. He really isn't. But he says it hurts awful, and when he says awful he means *awful.*"

"I don't doubt it. But I hear from my son Paul that you're still making early-morning basketball practice at school."

"Well, yes."

"I'll tell you what I think. This could be either a minor or a chronic muscle pain. Early-morning backache—is it early arthritis of the spine? I can't say. The only way to find out is to test. I think it's significant enough to warrant coming in to the hospital some weekend soon for some tests and X-rays. If they're positive for arthritis, then we'll know what to do. Why don't you-all figure out a good time and let me know. How's your little sister, Rick?"

"She's O.K., I guess."

"Actually, Doctor, she's been running a little sugar. Maybe I'd better bring her in."

"Maybe you'd better."


*Mrs. Lillie May Dunn, 72. Widow. Heart.*

"I've got some questions for you, Lillie May. It's been over a year since you've been in here—why? And when your sister made this appointment, she told me you'd stopped taking your blood-pressure pills—why?"

"I don't know. I never liked those pills, I guess."

"Well, how do you feel?"

"The same—terrible."

"In what way?"

"Like I got up early and worked hard all day long."

"Well, I guess you know what that feels like."

"I sure do."

"I'm going to check your blood pressure. You don't have to hold your breath. Mmm. O.K. Have you been sleeping all right?"

"I sleep all the time. I slept through the television yesterday afternoon. My favorite show, too."

"Are you short of breath?"

"Some."

"I'll tell you your trouble, Lillie May. You've been neglecting yourself. You've gone into heart failure. When I listen to your chest, I can hear a lot of what we call moist rales—a lot of mucus."

"Is that serious?"

"Of course it's serious. I'm going to send you to the hospital. You need some looking after."

"All right. But when?"

"In about an hour."

"From now?"

"That's right."

"How about tomorrow?"

"Tomorrow? You got something planned for this afternoon?"

"No. Oh, no—it isn't that. It just seemed so sudden."

*Mitchell Brininstool, 16. Father, head of X-L Transportation Co. Stomachache.*

"Elwood, I thought you'd better have a look at this boy."

"Right. What's your trouble, Mitchell?"

"He's got stomach cramps, Elwood, and he's nauseated and he's got diarrhea."

"What have you been eating, man?"

"Sometimes he eats what we eat and sometimes he eats junk. Teenage junk. I was worried about appendicitis."

"You want me to take his appendix out, JoAnn? Let's wait a minute. I ought to examine him first. Can you describe the pain, Mitchell? Where does it hurt?"

"It like comes and goes."

"That sounds like colic. Did you burp him, JoAnn?"

"It doesn't bother me at night. I sleep O.K."

"Well, seriously, I don't think it's appendicitis. The pain in appendicitis is right around—you don't mind if I draw a diagram on your belly? That kind of pain is around here. And yours is over here. Also, this is a colicky pain. It's a spasm—literally a nervous gut. It's probably emotional in origin. I'm going to give you a prescription for a gut sedative. That will quiet you down, and I think you'll stop hurting. You play basketball, don't you, Mitchell?"

"Yes, sir."

"As a matter of fact, you're one of the leaders?"

"Well, I'm the captain."

"Right. And you're a blood player, aren't you? You want to win?"

"Yes, sir. I guess so."

"And the Jal Panthers haven't had too good a season this year, have they?"

"No, sir. It's been real bad. We lost again on Monday."

"O.K., Mitchell. JoAnn, I guess I'll see you at Hal Baker's barbecue on Saturday. I hear he's barbecuing a goat."

"Yes. But, Elwood—my Lord! You mean Mitchell's trouble is nerves? You mean at sixteen years old he's got nerves? Just like all the rest of us?"


*Cynthia Hurta, 15. Father, grocery store. Sore eye.*

"It says here you've got a sore eye, Cynthia. Which eye?"

"It's this one—the left. I was helping Mom at the store, carrying stuff around, and, I don't know, maybe I got something in it, and I began to rub it and it was sore. That was last night."

"Let's take a look. Mmm. Right. You've got a nice little pimple there. But I need help—wait a minute. *Joan! Cecilia! Somebody!* Joan, I need you. Take this light. I'm going to nick the top off this pimple here. Now, hold the light—that's right. Now then."

"*Doctor!* You're not going to *cut* it off! With that *knife!* Oh, *no!*"

"Be quiet, Cynthia. You won't even feel it."

"Can't you use like a needle or something? Oh, Doctor—*please!*"

"There—it's done. What's the matter with you, Cynthia?"

"I guess I'm just a rotten coward."

"For heaven's sake. I wouldn't hurt you, baby. You know that."

"I thought you were going to like carve your initials."

"Nonsense. I like your sarape, Cynthia—all that fringe. *And* all those beads. They're delicious. You look good in beads."

"Good. Now, Dr. Schmidt, *you* hold still. I want to see how *you* look in love beads. Wow—you look terrific."

"Hey—I do, don't I?"

"Promise me you'll wear them?"

"I solemnly swear. Now, get out. I've cured you, baby. Go home."

Dr. Schmidt lives on a quiet street of mulberry trees and watered green lawns on the south side of town. The desert begins at the end of his street, and the nearest oil and gas plants are a couple of miles away and to leeward of the prevailing desert wind. His house is a rambling brick house with a walled garden in back and a big mimosa tree overhanging the front door. The door was opened by a boy in glasses and a Boy Scout T-shirt.

"This is Paul," Dr. Schmidt said. "Paul is my No. 1 son. No. 2 is Philip, and No. 3 is Tim. They're probably around here somewhere."

"They're out," Paul said.

A slim young woman with golden-red hair came into the room.

"And this is my wife," Dr. Schmidt said. "I'm home, Ila Fay. And I hope to God we've got time for a drink before supper. I'm just a little . . ."

"There's time," Mrs. Schmidt said. "You-all go in and sit down and I'll— *Elwood!* What in the world have you got around your neck?"

"Love beads, ma'am."

"Wow!"

"Yes. They're a present from a grateful patient—from Cynthia Hurta. She was that glad she survived a little operation this afternoon."

"Well," Mrs. Schmidt said. "Oh, Elwood—did Mrs. You-Know-Who call you?"

"No—why?"

"She called you here around noon. She said she was in pain. It was the most urgent, most unbearable distress. She said she was in such agony she could hardly hold the phone in her hand. I advised her to call the office. Then I went down to the store. And guess who I saw going into Susan's Beauty Parlor?"

We had our drinks in a family room that overlooked the walled garden. It was a big, comfortable room with a table set for supper at one end and a fireplace laid with piñon-pine logs at the other. A mounted nine-foot sailfish hung above the fireplace.

"That fish up there is documentary proof that I had a vacation once," Dr. Schmidt said. "I caught it—*Fay* and I caught it—down in Mexico. I was able to get me a locum tenens. I got my good friend Dr. Orene Whitcomb Peddicord, of Kermit, to look after my practice, and Fay and I had four fun-filled days and nights in Acapulco.

I'm not really complaining. I only mean that I'd like to be able to count on a day off every now and then. I truly enjoy my practice. I like taking care of Jal. I like being a G.P. I like the variety. I don't think I could stand the sameness of the specialties. I wouldn't want to look at hearts all day. Or urinary tracts. Or pregnant women. On the other hand, I know my limitations—in surgery, anyway. I'll do an appendectomy, if I'm satisfied it's necessary. I do Caesarean sections and hemorrhoidectomies. I do tubal ligations. I've got a D. & C.—dilation and curettage—scheduled for tomorrow morning. I don't do hysterectomies. I know when to refer, or defer, and— knock on wood and other superstitions—I've never had any serious trouble. I've never even had a malpractice suit. I think I'm a good family doctor. I think I do my job. But, you know, I sometimes wonder who in hell is going to take my place. Another G.P.? Not likely—we're a vanishing breed of cat. So who? A pediatrician? An internist? An obstetrician? A general surgeon? A dermatologist?"

The telephone rang. There was an extension on a table at Dr. Schmidt's elbow, and he answered it. He frowned. Mrs. Schmidt came in from the kitchen and stood in the doorway. Dr. Schmidt listened and nodded and grunted, and hung up.

"That was the hospital," he said, and got up from his chair.

"Oh dear," Mrs. Schmidt said.

"I know," he said. "But it shouldn't take too long. It's one of the Lister boys. They brought him in from wherever he works, and his mother is there, and she says he's ruptured himself."

"Well," she said. "There's no harm done. I haven't put the chops on yet. Just let me know when you're starting back."

I could hear somebody moaning and groaning as we came in the hospital door. A nurse was standing in the doorway of the emergency room. She gave Dr. Schmidt a knowing look. We went into the room. A young man in work clothes was lying on an examining table, and beside him stood a woman in a gray pants suit, with an elaborate pile of blond hair. She was holding his hand. When he saw us coming, he closed his eyes and opened his mouth and groaned.

The woman had a stricken look. "Oh," she said. "Oh, Dr. Schmidt."

"Well, Randy," Dr. Schmidt said. "Can you tell me what happened?"

"He was lifting a great big sack of cement."

"Can you tell me about it, Randy?"

"I—I guess so. But it's like Mom says. I was lifting this sack of cement and, I don't know, I got this terrible pain, and then I blacked out, and—Oh, it hurts. It *hurts*."

"Can you show me where?"

"Me?"

"Yes, Randy. Show me with your hand. I see. All across there? How about here? O.K. Now—can you sit up?"

"Ohhh . . ."

"O.K., Randy. That's enough. Well, what you've done is pulled a muscle down there. I don't believe you've got a rupture. I do believe you'll be all right. I'm going to give you a shot of Demerol to make you comfortable. That's just about all I can do."

"Are you going to keep him, Doctor?"

"You mean, admit him? Of course I'm going to admit him. He's hurt, and I want to be sure his trouble is what I think it is. Why?"

"Well, I'm just standing here thinking. You know, about the insurance. If he don't stay overnight, the insurance don't pay for any of this."

"I see. All right, Randy. The nurse will get you settled. I'll see you on evening rounds."

We walked back to the nursing station. There were two nurses there. One of them was an elderly woman in the Pink Lady uniform of a volunteer. Dr. Schmidt sat down at a desk and began filling out the admittance and order forms on Randy Lister. A teenage girl in jeans and a Jal Panthers football jersey came up the corridor.

"Dr. Schmidt?"

"Yes?"

"I'm Billy Will's friend—Billy Will Sharp?"

"Right."

"Yes. And Billy Will's hungry? He wants to know can I get him something to eat."

"Oh? And what's he hungry for?"

"He says he wants a cheeseburger."

"I see. And did he happen to tell you why I've got him here in the hospital?"

"Oh, sure. He's been having this pain in his stomach, and—"

"That's right. You tell him he can have a milkshake."

Dr. Schmidt went back to his forms. It was almost seven o'clock, and I was getting hungry myself. The telephone rang. The nurse answered it and looked at Dr. Schmidt.

"Are you here?"

"I guess so," he said, and took the receiver. "Hello? . . . Yes. . . . Oh—is that so? Mmm. Right. . . . Right. . . . O.K." He handed the receiver back to the nurse. He shook his head. "Son of a bitch," he said. "Here's a man with nothing wrong with him except he's drunk by noon every day of his life, and now his wife calls up— and call out the Marines! He's sick! He's got pains. He hurts. There are too many Goddamned people in this town who think I'm like that light switch over there on the wall. Switch it on. Day or night. Rain or shine. And I'll come running. But I *ain't* a switch. I got rights. I'm a hooman bein'."

"What are you going to do?" I said.

"Do?" he said. "About the son of a bitch? Why, I'm going over to see him."